Folk Tales fron
and the Wo.

Peter N. Walker is a successful thi..... w..ter, as well as the author of numerous best-selling books for Robert Hale, including *Murders and Mysteries from the Yorkshire Dales* and *Murders and Mysteries from the North York Moors*. As Nicholas Rhea he has written *Portrait of the North York Moors* and the popular 'Constable' series, which was recently adapted for television.

In 1982 he retired as an Inspector with the North Yorkshire police to concentrate on his writing. He is married with four adult children and lives in North Yorkshire.

Folk Tales from York and the Wolds

PETER N. WALKER

ROBERT HALE · LONDON

ISBN 0 7090 4763 0

Robert Hale Limited
Clerkenwell House
Clerkenwell Green
London EC1R 0HT

Photoset in Palatino by
Derek Doyle & Associates, Mold, Clwyd.
Printed in Great Britain by
St Edmundsbury Press Ltd., Bury St Edmunds, Suffolk.
Bound by Hunter & Foulis Ltd.

Contents

Author's Preface

The contrast between the bustling city of York and the rustic calm of the Yorkshire Wolds could hardly be greater.

On the one hand there are the city streets and tourist attractions which draw millions of visitors each year, while on the other there are wide open spaces with rolling hills, quiet villages and empty roads. York is known the world over, while the inner Wolds have yet to be discovered as they complement both the Yorkshire Dales and the North York moors in their beauty and interest.

Both York and the Wolds have a long and interesting history which has produced the inevitable wealth of folk stories. Some are based on little-known tales which have come to us by word of mouth down the ages, and others are well-documented in other publications.

This modest collection seeks to place on record some of the better-known tales as well as several which are less familiar. As with all collections of such stories, I have taken the liberty of using the so-called 'novelist's licence' to relate the stories in my own way and where there have been several versions of one yarn, I have produced a composite.

It is hoped that this collection will help to preserve these ancient tales.

Peter N. Walker

1 Atwick
The Haliwell Goblin

Tiny Atwick, with its splendid beach, lies some distance
from the Wolds on the edge of Bridlington Bay. It is
between Bridlington and Hornsea, some two miles north
of the latter, and is one of the many villages along this
coastline which have suffered the ravages of the
ever-encroaching North Sea.

Low cliffs of earth provide expansive sea views, and
nearby there is evidence of the beds of ancient inland
lakes. Years ago, the tusk of an elephant was unearthed
here, thus giving some idea of the long occupation of this
quiet coastline.

Along Church Lane, some distance from Atwick's
houses is the red brick church with a rather unusual but
picturesque gabled tower; the church was rebuilt in 1876
but lacks any objects of great interest, although its font
may have survived from a much earlier time. Parts of the
cylindrical font have a Norman appearance, but subsequent carvings make it impossible to determine its precise
origins. Those carvings or chisellings might have been
done much later to 'enhance' it, so giving it the fake
appearance of dating from the fourteenth century. The
church is thought to occupy the site of a former monastery
or some other early religious establishment, but no
remains have survived.

One interesting object in Atwick is the relic of an old
cross which stands among its pebble-built cottages. The
broken shaft and three steps remain while the stonework
has been scarred by generations of visitors who have
inscribed their initials upon it. The cross has long been a

meeting-place for young people, but for centuries has served another important and more official purpose.

Its position has made it a marker or datum post for measuring the rate of erosion along this coast. In Poulson's *History of Holderness* (1840), the cross was said, in 1786, to be 33 chains and 61 links from the sea. That was a little over 1,000 yards. In those times, the measurement of distance was done by actual chains comprising links of iron or steel. In the years which followed, the sea consumed the land at the rate of about two yards every year and by 1871, the cross was 836 yards from the sea. An Ordnance Survey map, revised in 1896, showed the cross to be three-eighths of a mile from the sea, that is about 660 yards and so there is some discrepancy between these distances because, by the time of World War II, that distance was said to be 730 yards. Today, some records say the datum post is only 400 yards from the sea but my car's speedometer said it was around 700 yards. Precise measurements are not easy to obtain, but one thing is certain – with each passing year, a further two yards of coastline are lost to the waves as the sea moves ever closer to Atwick's old cross.

You can get an impression of the scale of erosion by following Cliff Road past the old cross. The road ends abruptly on the edge of the cliff near a caravan park, for the portion of road ahead has literally been swallowed by the sea. Close to the shore, the sea is stained a muddy-brown colour due to its constant consumption of the landmass.

But there is more of interest in Atwick. In 1991, the village was judged pretty enough to represent the Yorkshire and Humberside region in the Britain in Bloom competition for small villages, and there is also a pleasing village pond with ducks.

In addition, Atwick boasts two folk stories, a large number for such a small place! One concerns the ghost of a headless horseman who is said to make regular appearances in the village, but his identity and the story behind these sightings remain unknown.

The other tale concerns the village well. It was probably the second of the village ponds which is at the bottom of the hill upon which the church stands. It was full of still water when I called. Many years ago, this was known as the Haliwell or Holy Well, 'halig' being an old word for holy. Local rumour said an imp or hob lived in this well. He was a type of goblin who liked the company of good children but who disliked naughty ones. If a child misbehaved, the goblin would inflict some minor punishment such as nipping the youngsters or smacking them.

When mothers sent their daughters to draw water from this spring or well, they were warned never to be naughty, otherwise the Haliwell Goblin would become angry and hurt them in some small way, perhaps making their hair become tangled or creating troublesome knots in their hair-ribbons. He would also make the water harmful so that it caused illness among those who drank it, and so the children of Atwick had to make sure they behaved themselves when working or playing around the village well.

2   Beverley
Sanctuary, Sisters and Saints

Although Beverley is modest in size, it has for centuries been a place of immense religious significance. It ranks alongside York and Ripon in the development of Christianity in the north of England.

It was also the county town for the East Riding of Yorkshire. As well as hosting a busy market, it houses the courts and county council offices and has produced a variety of industries ranging from cloth in medieval times via tanning to a trawler-building shipyard in more modern times. In 1974, however, boundary changes placed Beverley within the new county of Humberside although it continues to be the major town of East Yorkshire.

Beverley is a delightful mixture of ancient narrow streets and clean modern estates, with a range of buildings to span the period between. There are Georgian houses, shops with carved panels above their doorways, black-and-white half-timbered houses with gables, an old inn with a carved barge-board, a seventeenth-century Guildhall and the classically designed Sessions House dating from the last century. During a walk round the town, I found an old inn with stone floors strewn with straw and gaslights around the walls, its only source of light. There is much more of interest in this lovely old town.

Some believe the surrounding countryside to be flat and unimpressive, although it is fertile and highly productive. On the outskirts is Beverley Westwood, a huge area of common land given to the townspeople in 1380 by Archbishop Neville. Here, cattle continue to graze without fences and the 300-year-old race-course draws crowds from the whole of Britain. It celebrated its 300th anniversary on 22 September 1990, for it was on that date in 1690, as Beverley Corporation Great Order Book records, 'Liberty is given to make a convenient ground on the Westwood for a horse race, the surveyors to appoint posts to be used on that behalf.' On 15 July 1991, the winner of the 7.35 p.m. evening race, Croft Valley, was ridden by HRH The Princess Royal, who had earlier that day opened a £600,000 improvement scheme at Pontefract race-course.

It is the town centre which continues to be a major attraction, with its medieval buildings, superior churches and fine market-place with its handsome cross. This cross is in fact an open shelter with stone pillars which support a cupola roof, and it is adorned with stone urns, the royal arms of England and France, and the town's own coat of arms. This depicts a beaver above a lake, for it is a tradition that beavers once colonized the River Hull, and that the town is named after them.

Another source of its name is of great antiquity. At the time of Ptolemy, it was known as Petouaria and this was later to become Pedwarllech. This old name supposedly arose due to the four standing-stones which marked the town boundaries. Three of these stones can still be seen, but from the word Pedwarllech there came Bevorlac, which in turn has become Beverley. This may not be true, however, for there is considerable doubt that the name of Pedwarllech ever existed – even if the four stones did. Another name, in use during the eighth century, was Inderawuda; the Venerable Bede translated this as 'in silver Derorum' which meant 'in the wood of deer' or 'in the forest of Deira', Deira being a northern kingdom which was then covered by a dense forest.

Much evidence of Beverley's ancient history remains, such as the North Bar; out of five such medieval bars or gates, this is the only survivor and the town's buses once had roofs shaped to cope with the distinctive archway of this handsome entrance. Only two such buses remain and they are used for ceremonial occasions, other buses being banned from using the gate. It is a reminder of the time when Beverley was surrounded by a wall and a moat, while another such reminder is to be found in the three surviving crosses around the outskirts. These were sanctuary crosses – their remains can still be seen on the road between Beverley and Cottingham, near traffic-lights on the road to Walkington and at Killingwoldgraves near the bypass roundabout towards Bishop Burton. The fourth stone, now missing, stood on the northern approaches to the town just beyond the hamlet of Molescroft. It is thought to have been destroyed or buried during construction of the railway line.

But Beverley's stature is forever assured by its superb churches. Towards the northern end of the town is St Mary's church and towards the south is Beverley Minster which is, in fact, the parish church for Beverley. Its beauty rivals that of York Minster and this, combined with the splendour of St Mary's, enables Beverley to compete with any of Britain's ecclesiastical centres.

St Mary's dates from the fourteenth century and is regularly mistaken for the minster. From some points on the way into Beverley, the beautiful central tower of St Mary's, built in pale stone, appears above the trees with all the majesty of a cathedral; the tower is almost 100 feet high, the church has embattled and pinnacled walls and a superb south porch with buttresses, niches and pinnacles. Upon one of its arched doorways is the carving of a hare holding a staff and carrying a satchel – it was this figure which inspired Lewis Carroll to create the character of the March Hare in *Alice in Wonderland*. Carroll added a watch to the character.

It is not surprising that visitors believe they have seen the minster when they visit this splendid old church. If St Mary's was the parish or sole church of this town, it would undoubtedly draw visitors from afar, but it is overlooked by the magnificent minster. Dating from 1220, this splendid church, (which was never a monastery), is a focal point for visitors and local people alike.

Among its many treasures are the tomb of St John of Beverley; a shrine to the Percy family who were Earls of Northumberland; and the ancient Frithstool or Sanctuary chair which stands beside the high altar and is a reminder of its links with Athelstan, the first king of All England.

It is Athelstan and the tomb of St John (see Harpham) which provides us with one of Beverley's folk stories. John was a great saint, ranking with Cuthbert of Durham as a major saint of the north of England, and it was he who established a monastery in Beverley towards the end of the seventh century. He retired to that monastery after a busy life. Taught by St Hilda of Whitby, he was a man of great holiness, wisdom and learning, and one of his own pupils was the Venerable Bede who recorded the early history of the church in England. When John died, he was buried within the monastery he had founded; the rosary he used was buried with him, and he was canonized in 1037 by Pope Boniface VIII. Soon after his death, and indeed during his life, miracles were reported by those who sought his intercession or who made the pilgrimage to his burial-place.

In the ninth century, John's monastery and shrine were almost destroyed by the invading Danes, but it was to this tomb that Athelstan made his way a century later. He was in need of spiritual support and knew of the miracles which had been worked by St John.

Athelstan was the golden-haired grandson of King Alfred the Great and was born in AD 895, becoming the first king of England in 924 until his death in 939. In 934 Athelstan was on his way to fight the Scots, and he knew it was to be a fierce war. The prize for the victor was the throne of the whole of England, the first time that one man could claim to be king of All England. It was while camping at Lincoln *en route* to the north that a pilgrim told Athelstan of the miracles worked by St John of Beverley; the pilgrim himself claimed to have been restored to health after visiting the tomb. Athelstan, who believed in miracles and the power of God, decided to make a detour through Beverley so that he could pray at the famous tomb.

When he arrived, he prostrated himself before the shrine, and then took out his dagger and laid it on the high altar. Before God, he then swore that if he were successful in battle, he would return to Beverley to endow the church with funds. He took with him a banner depicting St John of Beverley and set off to engage in battle against King

Constantine of Scotland. The battlefield was called Brunanberg, and has never been satisfactorily identified – some authorities believe it was on the coast of Northumberland, others favour a site near Brough in Westmorland, while yet others are convinced it was in West Yorkshire, somewhere in the Rother Valley.

During his journey to the battlefield Athelstan was clearly a worried man, because at one point he fell to his knees to ask God for some sign that the Scots would be subjected to the kings of England. It is said that he 'smote a rock with his sword' and this caused a deep cleft to be made in the stone. That cut, an 'elme' in length, was visible for centuries afterwards (an elme or ell was an English measure equivalent to some forty-five inches in length). Some accounts say that this rock was actually in Scotland, near the castle at Dunbar, others that the town of St Johnstone in Scotland is named after the place that the Banner of St John was erected as battle raged.

Arguments over the precise site will continue, but the point is that Athelstan scored a powerful victory which was regarded by some as a turning point in our history. His fame spread – the Norsemen called him the Greatest European, the French regarded him as the Most Famous King of All Time, while others referred to the Battle of Brunanberg as the Great War or the Summit of the Horizon of the Western World. In some places, stone pillars used to support important buildings were named in his honour – they were called Athelstan's Pillars in praise of his strength.

There is no doubt that Athelstan was a hero of immense stature – and he believed that he owed it all to St John of Beverley.

In later years, many other sovereigns were to visit the shrine of St John to pray for similar favours. They included King John, Edward I, Henry IV and Henry V with his queen. William the Conqueror suffered a shock after sending members of his army to destroy the minster. But following Athelstan's success, the banner of St John was carried in many battles, including the Battle of the Standard at Northallerton in 1138. One story is that during the Battle of Agincourt in 1415, the victorious soldiers saw a ghostly white horse carrying St John of Beverley; it moved about their ranks to give them encouragement and strength to continue their fight for England.

But Athelstan did not forget his earlier promise and in 938 he returned to Beverley, this time as the first king of All England. He endowed the church with lands and granted it collegiate status. It was never a monastery after his time, but he also granted it right of sanctuary. Between 938 and 1540, therefore, the town was subjected to an influx of criminals, some of them dangerous, who flocked there to be granted sanctuary, or refuge from the law. They were allowed to remain there for up to thirty days with food and bedding provided and it was the duty of the canons of the minster to care for them. The canons had then to attempt to secure a pardon for each criminal and if this was not achieved within forty days, the criminal was escorted to the town boundaries to be confronted by the king's representative, the coroner and declared an outlaw.

Beverley was unique as a place of sanctuary because, thanks to Athelstan, it offered an alternative to outlawry. A criminal could instead become a frithman or grithman. This was done by securing two or even three periods of sanctuary and then promising to remain a 'servant of the church for life'. It meant residing within the town's limits, giving up all personal belongings and swearing allegiance to the town's authorities. As a consequence, Beverley became the home of rogues and villains from afar and their behaviour and presence caused much alarm and annoyance to the law-abiding folk. But sanctuary was abolished by Henry VIII during the Reformation and one reminder of that strange legal provision is the stone Frithstool which can still be seen on the high altar of Beverley Minster. The Frithstool might have been used by St John as his episcopal seat, and the fugitive had to sit in it in order to be granted this unique right. It is the oldest object in the minster and dates to the very foundation of the church.

The influence of Athelstan remains strong in Beverley, and in 1726 there was a great deal of excitement when a tomb was uncovered in the minster. It was known that St John's remains had been reinterred in 1023, but that the tomb had been destroyed by fire in 1188. Some remains were saved and placed in a further tomb, and in 1292 a silver shrine was constructed behind the altar to house them.

Then, in 1726, some men were relaying the floor and found human remains encased in lead. They also found a dagger. This led to speculation that these were the remains of St John and that this was the very dagger that Athelstan had laid on the altar in AD 934, each having been separately reinterred at a later date.

Another folk tale concerns William the Conqueror's link with Beverley Minster. When he was laying waste to the north of England, he sent to Beverley one of his military commanders, Toustain, with a complement of men. Their task was to take the town and destroy the minster. When the people realized that Toustain was approaching, they fled to the minster to gain sanctuary from the invaders, but the evil Toustain ignored this tradition. He led his soldiers to the huge church where the people had gathered and was about to violate the ancient right of sanctuary. But as he crossed the threshold, there was a tremendous flash of light and Toustain fell dead. His neck was broken and his head twisted around to face the opposite direction, while all his limbs had been reduced to mere stumps. His hands and feet had disappeared.

At this the soldiers fled and left the townspeople in peace, while William the Conqueror gave instruction that the people of Beverley should be allowed to continue their customs without interruption.

Yet another folk story is linked with Beverley Minster and its source can still be seen in the south aisle. This is the Two Sisters tomb, the resting-place of two unknown, unmarried women who were thought to have been benefactors to the town and the church but a mysterious tale surounds them.

Towards the end of the seventh and beginning of the eighth centuries, a powerful earl owned land in and around South Burton near Beverley. (After the Norman Conquest, the village name was changed to Bishop Burton by which it is still known, for it then belonged to successive Archbishops of York.) The earl was Earl Puch who had a delicate but lovely wife and two beautiful daughters whose names we do not know. Earl Puch had built a church in Bishop Burton and had arranged for the Bishop of York to come and dedicate the new building. At the time, the bishop was none other than the good John of Beverley. On the day of the ceremony, however, Lady Puch was ill and could not attend; the earl was tempted to cancel the ceremony but his wife insisted that it proceed because the people had been looking forward to it.

After the blessing of the church, the bishop came to dine with the earl, who asked if John would be kind enough to bless his wife with some of the holy water used at the church and perhaps pray over her so that she might effect a recovery. John agreed, and to the astonishment of all Lady Puch made an immediate recovery and in fact came down to join them at dinner, helped with the serving and then ate a hearty meal.

This remarkable recovery made a tremendous impression upon the earl's two daughters, both described as 'lovely, angelic girls beautiful in form and feature'. They regarded this as a miracle, for the holiness of John, the Bishop of York, was already renowned. The bishop blessed them too, and for years afterwards they ignored the attentions of the youths of the area and devoted their lives to charity and the church. Neither married, but worked hard for the poor and donated land and money both to the church and to the under-privileged of Beverley. They were true benefactors.

Eventually, their love of religion compelled them to enter a convent and so they became sisters in the convent that John had earlier founded in Beverley. It was on the site of the present minster.

Their decision was approved of by the earl, who gave the convent land, cattle and money. The only time they ventured outside its walls was to attend the funerals of their parents, and then a mystery occurred. It continues to be related even today, some 1,250 years later.

One Christmas Eve in the convent, the nuns were gathering for midnight mass when it was noticed that the two sisters were absent. The other nuns thought they had either fallen asleep or had forgotten about the mass, but as the girls had never missed an office or a service before, this was unlikely. Clearly, their absence was totally out of character and their colleagues became alarmed.

A search was made, but no sign of the sisters was found. The Christmas services continued without them, and although the nuns continued to search their convent and the outlying areas, no sign of them was discovered. The weeks became months and the girls had almost been forgotten when the abbess decided to visit the tower which overlooked the convent. She climbed the stairs, unlocked the door and there, wrapped in each other's arms, were the sisters.

At first the abbess thought they were dead, but they were alive; at the sound of her entry, they opened their eyes and one of them apologized.

'I'm sorry, Mother,' she said. 'We fell asleep for an hour, it must be time for midnight mass.'

'Midnight mass!' she cried. 'My children, it is not Christmas now, it is the sixth day of May ... you have been asleep for many months...'

'No, Mother,' one of them insisted. 'We have not been asleep, we have been to heaven.'

They then described a most beautiful place, with sights inconceivable to the human eye and music which was never heard in this lower life. They talked of a place with no water or land, no mountains or valleys, no lakes, trees or rivers, no material objects of any kind, but consisting of picturesque scenery, impalpable and cloud-like, of the most ravishing beauty, peopled by angelic beings and beatified mortals with gloriously radiant features beaming with happiness and peace.

They went on to say that they had met John of Beverley, whom they believed would one day be made a saint, and he had told them that their parents were in heaven, but that they would not be permitted to see them until they, too, had departed this mortal life. It was then realized by the abbess that the date of their discovery, 6 May, was the eve of the anniversary of the death of John of Beverley. He had died on 7 May 721. But how had they survived in a locked room without food or drink for more than four months?

Later, at a date which is not given in the legend, the
sisters did die and were laid side by side in a tomb within
the convent. But for fifty years afterwards, their bodies did
not decay.

Like St John's grave, their tomb became a shrine and a
place of pilgrimage, but in 1188 the church suffered
dreadfully from a fire and the tomb was destroyed. When
the new minster rose from the ashes of the old church in
1220, a tomb was prepared for their remains, for they had
escaped the worst of the fire. This was placed within the
new church, but was not inscribed with their names. It can
be seen today in Beverley Minster where it is known
simply as the Two Sisters Tomb; bread was once
distributed to the poor from its vicinity, thus continuing
their good work.

3 Bridlington
A Miracle Worker

In addition to John the apostle and John the Baptist there are dozens of other saints called John. Some sixty-four can be found in *The Roman Martyrology* alone, but three have associations with the East Riding of Yorkshire.

St John of Beverley was born in the village of Harpham (see Harpham) and died at Beverley in AD 721; St John Fisher was born at Beverley in 1469 and was martyred for opposing the reforms of Henry VIII; he was canonized in 1935. The third member of this local trio is St John of Bridlington. He was born at Thwing, a village thought to be the capital of the Wolds during the time of Danelaw. Its name may have associations with the Scandinavian 'things', which were judicial or legislative assemblies.

John was born around 1320, and died at Bridlington in 1379. He was canonized by Pope Benedict XIII in 1401. His adult life was spent as a monk in Bridlington's famous priory and eventually in 1363 he became its prior, although his life appears to have been quiet and prayerful. None the less, he was said to be the source of many miracles, some of which occurred after his death to people who had visited his tomb and shrine. Stories of some of those happenings are part of the town's lore (see also Langtoft).

Bridlington is one of the country's finest seaside resorts, known among other things for miles of sandy beach. The long bay is a sweeping arc of clean sand, while the town is a pleasant mixture of old and new. At one stage, there was a clear distinction between the two parts – the older town was known as Burlington, a name which still crops up

among the local people, while the harbourside was called
Bridlington Quay. Today, the whole town is called
Bridlington.

The newer portions are typical of a popular seaside
town and might not appeal to the more discerning – there
are the inevitable amusement arcades, bingo halls, gift
shops, sea food stalls, noise and bright lights, but there is
calm and quality to be found in the older part. The ancient
centre of Bridlington, known over the years as Brellintona,
Bridlingtonia, Burlinton, Burlington, Bretlinton or Bret-
lyngton, includes the original market town and priory.
There is a delightful cobbled market-place with elegant
lamp standards and a set of stocks, but the gem is the
priory. Although the original Catholic monastery was
almost completely destroyed by Henry VIII during the
Reformation, some of its remains have been utilized to
construct the present priory, which now serves as the
town's Anglican parish church. Henry is said to have
taken an eighth of a ton of silver from the ruined priory, as
well as a great deal of gold; the roof-lead was melted down
and the monastery barn, the largest in England, was
destroyed.

Also destroyed was the famous shrine of St John of
Bridlington, which had brought many pilgrims to the
town.

The priory and old town are some distance from the sea
but nearby one can find some fine gardens, fountains and
other imposing buildings, as well as some very peaceful
and quiet streets. The town has some interesting sundials
too – one is near the north pier and bears the phrase 'So
passeth the glory of the World', which is probably a
reference to the continuous passing of ships.

Bridlington has long been popular with visitors from
every class of society, from commoners to members of the
Royal family, and at one stage it drew the very best of
British society. Its more genteel side has attracted writers
and artists – Charlotte Brontë's first visit to the seaside
was at Bridlington and the sight of the bay created such
powerful emotions within her that she trembled and wept.

Another Yorkshire lady of achievement is commemorated here. Part of Bridlington is known as Sewerby

where, in Sewerby Hall, there is a display of memorabilia associated with an aviator from Hull, the famous Amy Johnson, who was honoured by a popular song called 'Wonderful Amy'. She made history when she flew solo from England to Australia and she followed that achievement with many other epic flights in the 1930s. She died in January 1943, when her plane crashed into the Thames estuary.

Bridlington's promenades are noted throughout the country while its harbour, like so many along this coast, is protected by two large piers which jut into the sea. The area around the harbourside is delightful, and it is here that the famous Gypsey Race enters the sea (see Gypsey Race).

Its seafaring men have earned the respect of all through their toughness, bravery and skill. This is especially true of the local lifeboat crews who have won scores of gallantry awards. Although the waters of Bridlington's expansive bay appear calm and untroubled, they can soon be whipped up by winds into ferocious and destructive waves, as proved by many a lost ship.

But not all the lifeboat stories are happy ones – in November 1897 a steamer called the *Bordeaux* struck some rocks during a ferocious storm in Bridlington Bay, near Flamborough, and then drifted towards Smethwick Sands. The Flamborough lifeboat had been launched but could not reach the ship, and Bridlington lifeboat officials decided not to launch their crew. They felt it was wiser to wait for a break in the weather. But when the boat was finally launched, it was too late; the *Bordeaux* had sunk with all hands. This dismayed the townspeople, some of whom paraded effigies of the lifeboat crew along the seafront and then burned them. Later, a public inquiry vindicated the officials' decision, but it does show the depth of feeling that can arise when lives are at risk from the sea.

Among Bridlington's seafaring tales is one which has survived for many years. It concerns a well-known Quaker called Robert Fowler, who in 1657 began to build a ship. He knew nothing about navigation or seafaring, but was determined to sail across the Atlantic to America.

And, being a man of determination, nothing would deter him from his goal. As he could not afford to buy or equip a suitable vessel, he set about constructing one of his own! When he had finished his ship, he then persuaded a further eleven like-minded Quakers to join him and so this little band of God-fearing men set sail. They had no sailing experience whatsoever – all they had to guide them was absolute faith and prayer! Much to the astonishment of everyone, they landed safely in America, only two miles from their intended destination!

It is another seafaring story which provides us with an astonishing yarn associated with St John. This event occurred while he was still alive and prior of the town. Five men set sail from Hartlepool to the north of the River Tees estuary. They went fishing but did not realize that the fresh breeze from the north was carrying them too far south. In time, the breeze grew stronger and was soon a powerful wind; only then did they realize that they had drifted further than they had intended and were now off the Yorkshire coast. As the wind grew to storm-like proportions it whipped the sail-securing ropes from their sockets and began to fill the little craft with sea-water.

The men began to grow alarmed as they were now off the coast of Flamborough, in seas notorious as a graveyard for greater vessels, and genuine panic began to take over from their hitherto controlled but urgent work.

But try as they might, they could not guide their sinking boat towards the shore. The seas were too strong, the winds too fierce, their boat was filling with water and defeating their attempts to ladle it out. It was clear that they were sinking and would all be drowned. Then they noticed the tall outline of the tower of Bridlington Priory. They had heard of the saintliness of Prior John and decided that prayer was their only salvation. Each man fell to his knees among the water which threatened to capsize their boat and destroy them.

There is little doubt that they thought they were facing death. But then something astonishing happened. Walking towards them across the tops of the waves came the figure of a monk; in spite of the gales and the turbulence about him, he continued walking until he reached their little boat. Then he put out a hand and gripped the bow, holding it firm. The men began to row and were astonished as the monk held the boat steady and guided them to the safety of Bridlington beach.

During his lifetime, St John is said to have performed other miracles – he raised no less than five people from the dead, restored the sight of a blind woman, and healed a lame man. These miracles continued after his death when his grave beame a shrine for the faithful, who endured long pilgrimages to visit it. But when Henry VIII 'reformed' the Church, he destroyed that shrine, although the name of Bridlington's own St John continues to be associated with this seaside town.

4   Burton Agnes
Lady Anne's Skull

The name 'Burton' appears in many East Riding villages, some examples being Brandesburton, Burton Constable, Burton Fleming, Burton Pidsea, Cherry Burton, Bishop Burton and Burton Agnes. The word burton probably comes from burhtun or burghtun, with burh or burgh being a village or community (from which we get the modern burgh or borough), while tun refers to a farm. Thus Burton implies that the village grew around a farmstead in bygone times. The various prefixes and suffixes provide an added identity to this oft-used village name. There are lots of other Burtons elsewhere in Yorkshire, including Constable Burton in Wensleydale which should not be confused with Burton Constable in the Wolds!

The following folk story, however, concerns Burton Agnes which, in the thirteenth century, was known as Burton Anneys, the suffix probably being associated with a prominent family who lived there. It has no connection with a lady called Agnes! Accounts of the modern Burton Agnes often describe it as a typical picture-postcard English village, for it is certainly peaceful, beautiful and interesting. Near the hall is a fine old church dedicated to St Martin, approached along an avenue of ancient clipped yews, past charming cottages, pretty gardens and a beautiful pond. Ponds are still a feature of several East Riding villages and the one at Burton Agnes is particularly charming.

The village stands on the A166 midway between Bridlington and Great Driffield, and is split by this busy main road which carries heavy coast-bound traffic during the summer months. For all its charms, it is upstaged by a particularly splendid building – Burton Agnes Hall, widely regarded as one of the finest Elizabethan houses in England.

But first, a look at the church. It is thought to date from pre-Conquest times, although much was rebuilt around 1125–40, with subsequent alterations throughout the centuries. Nevertheless, there are many Norman features, some of which have been incorporated within the existing building, such as the font and the south arcade which contains part of a Norman wall. The font, by the way, was discovered in the garden of the village rectory and returned to the church by Archdeacon Samuel Wilberforce (1805–73). He was vicar here and was the son of the famous William Wilberforce (1759–1833), whose campaigning led to the abolition of slavery; Samuel later became Bishop of Winchester.

The northern aisle dates from the fourteenth century while the tower and clerestory were added in the fifteenth. It is a veritable mixture of styles and periods but all the more interesting because of it; it also contains commemorative monuments to several local families. The more important include the St Quentins, Somervilles, Boyntons and Griffiths. Griffins can be seen too, for these were the emblem of the Griffiths family.

It is a member of the Griffiths family who features in a folk story which is for ever associated with Burton Agnes. There were two Sir Henry Griffiths, father and son, and one has left in the church a curious and somewhat gruesome monument to himself and his two wives. With regard to his wives, one bears the name Willoughby and the other Bellingham, but we are not given the Christian names of the ladies in question, nor are we provided with the dates of their deaths. Research has suggested that the Willoughby lady was called Mary, and the Bellingham one Dorothy, although official records of the era, including Burke's account of extinct baronetcies, do not show Sir Henry's second marriage. Some records suggest that Henry, the son, was never married. Thus these Henrys have left us with a puzzle as well as an impressive but sombre monument containing bones, skulls and black coffins among its heraldic splendour.

The Griffiths family is steeped in history; the first Sir Walter was born in 1481 and married Joan Nevill, a granddaughter of the first Earl of Westmorland and great-granddaughter of John of Gaunt. The first Henry married Elizabeth Throckmorton to produce his son, also called Henry and it was the former who built the stunning red brick mansion which has earned such glowing praise throughout the centuries. There has been a house on this site since Norman times, and an interesting portion of a former Norman manor-house survives in the courtyard. It is in the care of English Heritage and entry is separate from the hall.

Building of the present Burton Agnes Hall started very late in the sixteenth century, around 1598, and dates such as 1601, 1602 and 1603 appear on the doorways and lead rain-water pipe-heads. There is a picturesque gate-house with rounded arches and octagonal towers which bears the arms of James I and the date 1610; this arch leads into the grounds surrounding the hall, while the arms of Elizabeth I are above the entrance to the house itself. The gardens are replete with ancient yews, neatly trimmed, and until two centuries ago there was a bowling-green in the forecourt. There is now a croquet lawn just within the gate.

The house is exquisitely furnished and boasts some magnificent carved chimney-pieces and a highly elaborate oak staircase on pillars. One of the chimney-pieces depicts a curious dance of death in which a skeleton is shown dancing over symbols of earthly power such as a papal crown, an imperial crown and the symbols of war. This unique work is carved from one piece of oak.

This splendid house passed into the Boynton family by marriage in 1613 and has since been passed down the family. It remains in private hands, but is open to the public; potential visitors are advised to check the precise opening times.

The Sir Henry who built the house is featured in a curious folk story. It dates from the seventeenth century when three sisters lived in this house. They were fine-looking girls. A portrait of them still exists and hangs in the inner hall; it depicts three tall, slender and handsome young women in Elizabethan dress, with the youngest standing on the right of the picture. She was called Anne and is shown in dark mourning-clothes. She and her sisters were present as the house was being constructed, for they were Sir Henry's daughters, Frances, Catherine and Margaret, but Catherine was sometimes known as Anne. Some accounts suggest the three girls even helped to organize the construction of the house.

Anne became devoted to the superb building which was to become her home, but before it was completed she paid a visit to the St Quentin family who lived nearby at Harpham. Their house was slightly over a mile away (see Harpham), and while Anne was on her return journey, she was savagely attacked and robbed. We do not know whether her attackers were ever brought to justice, but the vicious assault left her close to death.

Fortunately, she was discovered by friends and carried home where she lay in a semiconscious, half-delirious state for some days. Some accounts say that the attackers raided the house and injured Anne when she tried to defend it, but other accounts suggest the assault occurred during the journey mentioned above. The scene of her attack can be seen today in the lane called Low Road, near St John's Well at Harpham. The site, surrounded by iron railings and covered with a small stone cupola, is inscribed 'St John's Well', and was flowing with water when I arrived in August 1991, even though other streams had dried up during that long, hot late summer. Last century, the cupola was damaged and was replaced by the one which can be seen today.

The precise details of her attack may not be too important to us, but as she lay seriously ill in bed, Anne must have feared she was about to die. She made it known to her sisters that she would never rest until some part of her body could remain 'for ever within our beautiful home as long as it shall last.'

That was her wish, and it was a wish she was to repeat until her death. Her sisters, fearing her morbid wishes were the result of her delirium, did not pay too much attention to her urgent words and Anne died without leaving that room. Today it is known as the Queen's Bedroom and contains a most elaborately decorated ceiling, which bears a unique plaster design of honeysuckle with interlacing branches. Close examination will show that some of the honeysuckle stems are suspended free of the ceiling.

The unfortunate outcome was that Anne's desperate wishes were ignored and she was buried within the village churchyard. Following her funeral, the house became the scene of what can only be described as ghostly manifestations or the presence of a poltergeist. Doors were heard to crash open and shut without explanation, furniture toppled over, there were weird groans and sighs throughout the building and sightings of a ghostly figure. The two surviving sisters then recalled Anne's wishes and began to wonder if she was haunting her former home. Deeply worried, they consulted their vicar and he decided that the only remedy was to obey Anne's wishes. A part of her body would have to be returned to the house.

Then followed the most traumatic experience – Anne's grave had to be opened so that a piece of her body could be removed, but when this happened, her body was found to be incorrupt. There were no signs of decay – except for her head. This had become detached from her trunk and was already skeletal, and so was regarded as a supernatural sign.

The head was removed from the grave and Anne's remains were carefully reburied. The head was carried into the house and the weird, unexplained noises and occurrences ended.

But when new residents occupied the house, they discovered the skull and, not knowing its history or purpose, relegated it to an outbuilding. The upheaval was renewed; the skull was brought back. With further new occupants, it was again taken out and buried, but each time this happened, the haunting, noises and general mayhem resumed. It was therefore decided that the skull must be placed within a wall so that it could never be removed. This was done, and since that time, none of the old troubles have recurred. No one knows precisely where the skull is hidden; some believe it is within the walls of the bedroom in which Anne died, others suggest it might be within the walls of the magnificent Great Hall.

But Burton Agnes Hall is now at peace – except for the occasional sighting of a ghostly Blue Lady in the Queen's Bedroom.

5   Burton Fleming
The Fairy Cup

Between Burton Fleming and Wold Newton there is a noted barrow called Willey Howe, which is said to be the grave of an ancient British chieftain (see Wold Newton).

The village of Burton Fleming is also known as North Burton (see Burton Agnes). It appears that the former name has been in use since the thirteenth century, while the latter came into use in the Tudor period. Both names are given on many maps, although for a time in the fourteenth century it was also known as Burton Splenyng. An old account says, 'It was commonlye cal'd Northe Burton as early as 1598.'

No less than six country roads lead into this tiny place. It occupies a pleasing position on a broad plain in the Wolds, some six miles inland from Bridlington.

The village is on the route of the famous Gypsey Race stream (see Gypsey Race), which was dry when we arrived in late August. We found a pleasant inn called the Burton Arms and a pond near the church; there is another pond in Back Street, while the old water-pumps and delightful cottages give the village a truly rural appeal.

The church, a curious mixture of brick and stone with a squat tower, has as tumbledown appearance, but it dates from Norman times and has a font from the period, as well as some thirteenth-century work, including a door and a chancel arch. One report says that it was 'churchwardenized' and patched up with bricks; close examination will reveal a blocked-up priest's doorway and a mutilated south doorway dating from the thirteenth century.

Nearby is an old manor-house, later a farm, at which

Queen Henrietta Maria, wife of Charles I, stayed the night of 5 March 1642, after landing at Bridlington during the Civil War. Her visit is recorded in the parish register as 'The Quene Majesty did lie at north burton with her army the 5 of March, 1642.'

Her night at Burton Fleming followed her unscheduled arrival at Bridlington. She was on her way from Holland with arms and ammunition to join Charles at York and her ship was scheduled to dock at Newcastle upon Tyne.

But heavy storms drove her ship, and the convoy which escorted it, to shelter at Bridlington, then known as Burlington. News of this reached Admiral Bolton or Batten who was hunting her, and he sent four of his ships to capture her. But after landing at Bridlington she took shelter in a house, still known as Queen's House, which overlooked the harbour; this was shelled by the admiral's ships but the queen escaped the bombardment by seeking shelter in a ditch. A report of the time says:

> Before she was out of her bed, cannon bullets whistled so loud about her, which musicke you may easily believe was not very pleasing to Her Majestie, that all her company pressed her earnestly to get out of the house, their cannon having beaten downe all the neighbouring houses, and two cannon bullets falling from the top to the bottome of the house where she was. Clothed as she could, she went on foot some little distance out of the towne, under the shelter of a ditche as the cannon balls fell thick about us. A sergent was killed within twenty paces of her ... we, in the end gained the ditche whilst their cannon plaid all the time upon us, the bullets flew for the most time over our heads, some grazing the ditch where the queen was...

They remained in the ditch for two hours while the seafront houses suffered terrible damage; then the ships withdrew and Henrietta escaped. In her haste to get away, she left her little dog behind.

She remembered in time and ran back for it, but we are not told whether it accompanied her to Burton Fleming. In this lovely village, she surely found a period of peace before her arrival in York on 9 March 1642.

A short distance away from Burton Fleming, towards Wold Newton, is the grave mound known as Willey Howe. Although an unsuccessful attempt was made to excavate the barrow in 1857, it is thought to be a burial-mound dating from prehistoric times. The area has many similar mounds because this part of Yorkshire is known to have been occupied by primitive man since the very earliest times.

Not surprisingly, there is a folk-tale associated with this mound. Its shape and mere presence must have exercised the curiosity of the local people for many centuries. The story is told by a monk called William of Newburgh who was born in Bridlington in 1136. He was a canon of Newburgh Priory near Coxwold in the twelfth century, and is known as an important chronicler and historian of the region. One of his works was *Historia Regum Angliae* – a history of English affairs.

According to William, a man was riding his horse late at night when he chanced to pass along the lane which runs beside Willey Howe. In the still darkness, he heard music and when he investigated the source, found an open doorway which revealed the interior of the mound.

He could peer directly into the depths and by the light of many candles within, saw a large gathering of tiny people seated around a table. They were enjoying a great feast. The hall was sumptuous in its furnishings and the table laden with the finest of food and wine. The party laughed and sang to cheerful music and there was a very happy atmosphere.

The man, who is not named, stood bewitched, for he knew that this was the reputed haunt of fairies and that he must not intrude, but he must have kicked a stone or coughed because the company noticed him outside. He was still astride his horse. One of them came out and advanced towards him carrying a goblet, but he could not flee because he was transfixed with curiosity, or even fear. The cupbearer seemed friendly and handed him the goblet, asking him to take a drink.

But the man was terrified; he had heard awful stories of what happened to anyone who drank with the fairies. If you drank with them, it was said, they gained total power over you.

Tense with fear, he reached out and accepted the goblet, but then the spell was broken. He kicked his horse into action and galloped off, still clutching the cup in his hands while emptying its contents on to the ground. There was an immediate angry outcry as the band of fairies abandoned their feast to pursue him, but he was on a fast horse and was able to outdistance them.

He knew that the goblet was precious – if it belonged to the fairies, it would possess magical qualities and would be manufactured from magical ingredients. The man did not know what to do with the precious cup and, after a lot of consideration, decided to present it to his king – Henry I.

Henry, who reigned from 1100 to 1135, retained the fairy cup and then gave it to King David of Scotland. We are not told what King David did with it, but later, when Henry II expressed a wish to see this magic cup, it was given to him. There has been very little information about it since that time, the twelfth century, but the story was resurrected in 1857 when it was said that the goblet was not made from any magical substance but consisted of fairy gold – a cheap, worthless metal.

My sources do not reveal the present whereabouts of that goblet, although in 1874 it was suggested that it was still in existence, having then been handed down from one generation to the next for more than 700 years.

6 Filey
The Mark of the Devil

In the space of little more than a century, Filey grew from a small East Yorkshire fishing village into a thriving and popular seaside resort. It has attracted genteel people from all over Yorkshire – Charlotte Brontë once came here for a holiday – but following World War II the town found itself busy with more boisterous visitors who flocked to the holiday camps which were established nearby. Some of these have disappeared while others have been created, but Filey remains a pleasant mixture of old and new in its prime position between Scarborough and Bridlington. And it continues to attract a wide spectrum of visitors, either on a daily basis or for longer periods.

The town occupies a sheltered position to the north of Filey Bay, with extensive sea-views towards Filey Brigg. It is readily accessible and until 1974 stood on the boundary between the East and North Ridings of Yorkshire. The dividing-line between the two counties was a deep ravine. Today, Filey lies within the county of North Yorkshire although it is situated just off the north-eastern tip of the Yorkshire Wolds.

There is ancient history here. One enduring story is that Filey Bay featured on a map of the world produced by the Greeks.

Ptolemy is said to have indicated that this was his 'well-havened bay' to the north of Ocellum. Ocellum was probably Flamborough Head and it is known that Roman ships used the bay. A Roman pier was found there, Roman coins have been found upon the brigg and there is also evidence of the presence of a Roman lighthouse or beacon. Some of its stones survived and were placed in Crescent Gardens, one bearing carved figures of animals.

The church of St Oswald is more than 800 years old, with many alterations carried out through the centuries, and on the wall of the south aisle you can see a strange stone character with a big nose and long sleeves. His head rests on some cushions but no one is certain of his identity – one possibility is that he was a boy bishop of Filey some seven centuries ago. If so, he would have served as bishop only between 6 and 24 December in his year of election, as was then the custom: the fact that his effigy has been installed would suggest that he died whilst in office. Another feature of the church is the Fisherman's Window. This depicts Christ calling Simon Peter and Andrew, and was donated by the people of Filey in honour of townsmen who have been lost at sea.

The interesting red brick Catholic church of St Mary stands high above the bay, and the old town contains some quaint cottages and streets. One house bears the date 1696 and the inscription 'The Fear of God be in you', while the old main street runs directly down to the superb beach. It is from here that one becomes aware of the splendour of the wide bay with its broad and curving sweep of smooth sand.

To the south is the series of chalky-white cliffs for which Filey Bay is renowned and also the world famous bird sanctuary of Bempton Cliffs (see Flamborough); along the top of the cliffs are walks with stunning sea-views.

To the north lie Scarborough and several smaller bays, such as Gristhorpe Bay, Cayton Bay and Cornelian Bay, the latter being known for stones such as the cornelian, jasper and moss-agate, all once found here and used in the manufacture of jewellery. Filey Bay is stunning, and to its north the land juts into the sea at a point known as Carr Naze, from which extends an astonishing ridge of low rocks. These form the famous Filey Brigg, the word 'brigg' meaning bridge. This is not a bridge, however, but a reef of countless rocks which has been here for centuries. In the seventeenth century, it was known as Phelaw Bridge and one theory is that the word 'file' referred to this long slip of land and that Filey obtained its name from it. This is probably speculation on the part of an early travel writer. However, the brigg forms a natural breakwater for the sea and although it is covered at high tide, it is visible when the tide is low. It was visible when I called, a long slender finger reaching into the North Sea.

The brigg extends for several hundred yards and it is possible to walk along it, bearing in mind that one will have to cope with the uneven and at times slippery surface, as well as many holes, pools, channels and other hazards. These are a rich haven for marine life but the main factor to bear in mind, however, is that it does very quickly become covered at high tide and so one should never linger there unnecessarily as the tide comes in. When the sea is rough, it is wise not to venture out there at all, mindful of the fact that massive tidal waves are not unknown.

The brigg is a constant source of attraction for visitors, but the real time to witness this amazing path of rocks is probably during the winter months, when the sea is heavy with the rising and falling waves. It is one of the sights of Filey to see huge waves crashing over the brigg, sending sprays of sea-water high into the air and filling the bay with the roaring noise of the powerful water.

The origin of the brigg was a puzzle to our ancestors, and in the absence of any genuine knowledge they believed it had been built by the devil. We are not told why he would want to construct this highway into the waves, but the story of that work is linked to marks which are found on one of our best known sea-fish, the haddock.

On each side of a haddock's body, on the shoulders behind the head, are dark marks which look just like a pair of thumbprints and fingerprints. It is almost as if someone has gripped the fish with a thumb and forefinger at this point, and that the pressure of that grip has left its mark. The story is that the devil was busy building Filey Brigg when he lost hold of his hammer. It fell into the sea and he leapt in to grab it before it fell to the bottom. In his haste, he missed the hammer and caught hold of a passing fish. It was a haddock – and ever since that time, every haddock has borne the devil's fingermarks. It will bear them until the end of time, while Filey Brigg is alternatively known as the Devil's Bridge.

One curious addition to the story is that when the devil realized his error, he cried out, 'Ah, Dick!' from which we get the name haddock!

7 Flamborough
Tales of the Sea

Flamborough Head juts into the North Sea to the north-east of Bridlington, while the village after which this promontory is named reclines a short distance inland. This enormous and highly visible slab of land, like some gigantic nose, has been a landmark for centuries and is said to be the boldest that lies between the Tweed and the Thames. It was known to the Romans and to the Vikings, and it has now been appreciated by generations of visitors and residents alike for it offers some of the finest sea-views in Britain and presides over the wrecks of countless ships and boats.

The white cliffs are stunning and are riddled with caves and deep bays, two of which are called South Landing and North Landing. North Landing is especially popular with visitors; there is a carpark at the top and a steep climb to the sheltered sandy beach below. There, the lifeboats, fishing-cobles, caves and sand provide a source of constant interest.

While it is the mystique of Flamborough Head and the incredible coastline that has given rise to the inevitable folk stories, the village itself is worthy of exploration. It is large by comparison with many Wolds villages and is a pleasing mixture of old and modern buildings, some built of white chalk, with the inevitable hotels, boarding-houses and lighthouse.

There is a definite flavour of the sea here, with crabs, lobsters and seafood being sold on the streets as sea-birds wheel and cry above. And when we heard the familiar sound of an emergency-vehicle siren, it was not the police or the ambulance, but the coastguard being summoned for help.

The beautiful church of St Oswald, the patron saint of fishermen, is located on the edge of the village and is full of interest. It once had a wooden belfry and has Norman origins, although some of its fabric dates from the thirteenth century. Many surviving portions are from the fifteenth century, while the font and the chancel arch are Norman. There is an interesting window depicting a ship, while a patch of the graveyard has been set aside for the disposal of cremated remains. The church contains a remarkable fifteenth-century oak roodscreen and roodloft which may have come from Bridlington Priory, having been rescued during Henry VIII's Reformation. It is one of only two such screens which survive in Yorkshire. The other is at Hubberholme in Wharfedale.

Also inside are reminders of those great families of the Wolds, the Constables and the Stricklands. The Constables are one of the great landowners of East Yorkshire and lived at Flamborough as early as the thirteenth century. One of them was the fierce, warrior-like 'Little' Sir Marmaduke whose tomb lies to the left of the altar. His nickname belied his valour for he was still fighting at the age of seventy – he fought at Flodden Field and wielded a savage sword at that age! His life covered the reigns of six monarchs, many of whom praised his valiant work on their behalf. Some accounts say he died in 1518 while others suggest it was 1530, but a brief résumé of his career is given on the brass plaque above the tomb.

One story about him is that he died after swallowing a live toad while taking a drink of water. The toad ate his heart and killed him. That story is commemorated on his tomb where stone representations of his breast apparently lie open to reveal his stone heart. One lump of stone is said to represent the toad!

Another story of Sir Marmaduke has also entered local folklore. He knew that his family had lived in Flamborough since the thirteenth century, and they were probably there much earlier. He knew also that the Danes had invaded the coastline long ago and had claimed much of the land. As a consequence, it was one of his jokes that he said he never knew to whom the Constable family should pay their rent! He often said it was really owed to the king of Denmark and so, every year, he would walk to the top of the cliffs at Flamborough, tie a golden sovereign to an arrow and fire it as far as possible across the waves towards Denmark. He then shouted, 'That is an instalment of my rent! If anyone cares to come for that coin, I shall be ready to pay the balance that is due, and I shall pay it to the king of Denmark.'

Sir Marmaduke's son Robert died a Catholic martyr's death, being executed by Henry VIII because of Robert's powerful actions against the king's closure of the Catholic monasteries. His body was hung from the highest gate in Hull. Other members of the Constable family have involved themselves in historic and national events, not least Sir William who fought with valour at Marston Moor and also signed the death-warrant of Charles I.

One feature inside the church is the beautiful Flamborough Book of Service. This comprises illustrated panels on a wooden stand, and it commemorates everyone from the village who worked to win World War II. It is the painstaking work of Mr A Cracroft, and each panel is immaculately coloured and lettered as it honours the work of all, ranging from the WI, Home Guard, police and coastguards, to canteen workers, schoolchildren and members of the knitting league.

The Stricklands, who lived at nearby Boynton, were a powerful local family too and Walter Strickland also signed the death-warrant of Charles I. There is a strange tale about this, because it seems that when the Crown was restored, Walter was given a royal pardon for that action. This had been forgotten until 1936! By chance, the vicar of Flamborough was cleaning out a safe in the church when he found an old document. It was the actual pardon granted by Charles II to Walter Strickland in 1660, having lain there for 276 years. It was in perfect condition and is now in the County Archives at Beverley. A photocopy and a translation hang in the nave of the church.

The Stricklands were heavily involved in national and local affairs. Sir Charles is said to have been the model for Martin in *Tom Brown's Schooldays*, while William introduced the turkey to this country. William sailed from Bristol with Sebastian Cabot, and when the explorer discovered some large and curious birds, he decided to bring samples back to England for breeding. Young Strickland got the task of caring for them on board ship, and also had to look after them when they returned to Britain. Later, when he applied for a coat of arms for the Strickland family, he incorporated a turkey and the drawing of that turkey is said to be the world's first illustration of this bird.

But if Sir Marmaduke felt he owed something to the Danes, he was correct in their colonization of this part of England in the ninth century. Even so, he and many others were wrong in believing that the Danes built the mighty Danes' Dyke which forms an earth-barrier on the approach to Flamborough Head. Some 2½ miles long, this enormous earthwork reaches from Bempton Cliffs in the north to Sewerby Rocks in the south, effectively crossing the whole of Flamborough Head inland. Sixty feet wide in places and almost twenty feet deep, this long ditch is thought to be the work of the Brigantes who occupied the territory some 2,000 years ago; it may even be the work of Stone Age or Bronze Age man. There is no doubt that it is a defensive structure designed to seal off the inland regions from raiders who might land at Flamborough Head.

But persistent legend about its construction and purpose has led to it being erroneously called Danes' Dyke, while the stretch of land around it and on the seaward side, separated by the dyke from the rest of Yorkshire, has long been known as Little Denmark.

It is the jutting piece of land east of Flamborough that the world knows so well. Sheer, lofty white cliffs of chalk rise from the North Sea to form an irregular sequence along the shoreline between Filey and Flamborough. These cliffs are noted for the sea-birds which breed here – thousands of guillemots, puffins, kittiwakes, razorbills and gulls of various kinds, all protected by law. It was from these high cliffs that egg-collectors would hang on long ropes as they collected the eggs of sea-birds to sell in the cities, a practice that is now illegal. One of these nesting sites, Bempton Cliff, is the only mainland site in

Britain where gannets now breed and it is also protected by law.

The cliffs are now a reserve of the Royal Society for the Protection of Birds, complete with reception and information areas from where one can obtain up-to-the-minute reports about the birds. We arrived as the gannets were completing their breeding-season, but the fascinating little puffins had left. In summer-time the cliff-tops are rich with yellow gorse flowers, but below there are several dramatic bays, some sheltered by tall buttresses of chalk. On the edge of the village there is an ancient chalk tower known as the old lighthouse, although its presence and purpose has always been a mystery.

Pillars of chalk are a feature of this coastline, but the folk-tales concern the strange caves which riddle the cliffs at this point. They reach deep under the landmass and echo to the sound of the waves; truly, this part of the shoreline is like a honeycomb of caves and it does not take any great imagination to believe that they were once the haunt of smugglers. Most are large enough to accommodate a fishing-coble, and they have been given names. There is the inevitable Smugglers' Cave and others such as St George's Hole, Brail Cave, Church Cave, China Hole, Pigeon Cote, the Dancing School and more. Perhaps the most famous is Robin Lythe's Cave, sometimes called Robin Lythe's Hole, which has a ceiling some fifty feet high. This is the haunt of the legendary smuggler, Robin Lythe, but in spite of his fame, no one knows with absolute certainty whether Lythe was an actual person or a mythical figure.

He could be a folk hero who has grown from local smuggling tales, but he does feature as a pirate and smuggler in a novel, *Mary Anerley* by Richard D Blackmore, published in 1880. Blackmore achieved everlasting fame with his classic *Lorna Doone*, but he was also responsible for elevating the mysterious Robin Lythe to the status of a folk hero.

Others believe that Lythe was an honest sea-trader who made use of this coastline and whose life has been misinterpreted due to a combination of Blackmore's novel and local folk-tales. Even so, it is stressed by many local people that he did use the cave which bears his name, albeit accidentally; he had been shipwrecked off Flamborough Head. He managed to reach the shore in a state of near-exhaustion and succeeded in gaining access to the huge cave. There he spent some time regaining his strength before clambering high onto Flamborough Head to tell the world that he was alive.

One legend says that Robin Lythe's cave extends a great distance inland and that there is a secret exit somewhere in the countryside at the edge of the Wolds. This adds strength to the countless tales of local smuggling. According to other stories, Robin Lythe was a pirate and smuggler of great skill and enterprise who actually lived in this cave. It was the headquarters of his operations, from where he would keep watch for vessels with rich cargo as they sailed along the coastline. Once he had selected a suitable victim, he would relentlessly hunt it down until he acquired the riches it carried.

Then he would return to his cave and secrete the plunder in the maze of tunnels which were like a giant rabbit-warren in the cliff. Only he knew the way around the maze; the customs officers who tried to locate his hidden wealth were always defeated by the labyrinth of tunnels and none found his secret exit deep in the Wolds countryside behind Flamborough. Because of this, Robin Lythe became a rich and successful man. So the story says!

Another tale is that a vast secret hoard of pirated gold- and silver-plate and coins lies hidden somewhere within those caves. Many have attempted to locate it, but so far without success.

Another seafarer associated with Flamborough and the East Yorkshire coast is the notorious pirate, Paul Jones. It was off Flamborough Head that he fought an amazing and desperate battle with two English ships. The fight was later to be novelized by James Fennimore Cooper (1789–1851), a former midshipman whose many books included *The Pathfinder* and *The Deerslayer*. In this case, the story appeared in his second novel, *The Pilot*, published in 1823.

The famous true incident happened one evening in September 1779 while Paul Jones was commanding a small squadron of four ships. His own was called the *Bonhomie Richard*, a French East-Indiaman, and the others were the *Alliance*, an American frigate and two French ships, the *Pallas* and the *Vengeance*.

Off the coast of Flamborough, Jones encountered a convoy of English merchant ships escorted by the *Countess of Scarborough*, commanded by Captain Percy and the *Serapis*, commanded by Captain Pearson. When Jones made it clear that he intended to fight for the wealth they carried, Pearson ordered the convoy of merchant ships to flee and he managed to detain the pirate as the intended victims made for the safety of Bridlington harbour.

Jones was therefore left with no option but to engage the two escort ships in a fierce sea-battle. We are not told whether the three other ships which accompanied Jones joined the battle, but the fighting which followed was as fierce and as deadly as any seen at sea. It continued for several hours, but Captain Pearson erred by allowing Jones close enough to grapple his vessel and so the two ships were locked together.

A bomb or large hand-carried explosive was thrown down the main hatch of the *Serapis* and when this exploded it detonated a huge store of ammunition in the hold. The result was a massive explosion that severely damaged all three ships and caused a large number of deaths on both sides. In the midst of this mayhem, the pirate's master-gunner thought the battle was over and hauled down the pirate's flag. But Jones insisted that the battle was not over and continued the fight. The noise and drama alerted the people of Flamborough and the news soon reached the surrounding villages. Thousands of people turned out to watch and they crowded along the cliff-tops as the contest continued by the light of the September moon.

In the end, the pirate won and the English captains were forced to withdraw, but they had saved their fleet of merchant ships from capture. But Jones' happiness in victory was to be short-lived – very soon afterwards, his damaged but victorious *Bonhomie Richard* sank to the bottom of the North Sea. But luck was on Jones' side – he escaped to continue his piratical activities. Captain

Pearson was knighted by King George III for his part in saving the merchant ships and the merchants of London also honoured him by presenting him with a decorative sword.

But Flamborough was not the only local port which has reason to remember Paul Jones. It seems he enjoyed working along this coastline even though he was not particularly welcome. Near Mappleton, the East Yorkshire village between Hornsea and Withernsea which is slowly disappearing due to the action of the sea, there lived William Brough, a marshal of the High Court of the Admiralty. His home was Rolston Hall and its splendid windows overlooked the North Sea.

Jones hated Brough, probably due to his official position in matters affecting maritime law, and every time the pirate sailed along this coastline, he loosed a shell at Brough's house. We are not told how many of them scored a direct hit, although reports of the time suggest it was very few.

It is feasible that Paul Jones never intended to actually hit the mansion. Perhaps he regarded his pot-shots as a piece of light-hearted entertainment? None the less, for many years after Jones' death, a large stone marked the landing-place of one of those shells. It was in a field close to Brough's house.

With such a dramatic coastline, there are more folk-tales about Flamborough. One concerns the appearance of a headless woman who haunts the headland from time to time, and another is a ghostly White Lady who frequents Danes' Dyke. In the church there is a pair of white gloves which have associations with her. Years ago, it was customary for a maiden's coffin to be carried by women, and for the procession to be led by a girl carrying a pair of white gloves, sometimes made of paper. In 1761, there was such a funeral at Flamborough. The dead woman was a Miss Major and it seems that she and her betrothed had decided to seek the ghost of the White Lady. No one knows the outcome of their hunt, but Miss Major died very soon afterwards. The white gloves now in the church were used at her funeral, and that was the last time the custom was practised in Flamborough.

There is another haunting which frightened local children. It is the story of Jenny Gallows, sometimes called Jenny Lind. She is said to have died beside a road near Flamborough; a hollow still marks the place.

She hated noisy children and after her death, her wicked spirit continued her dislike of being disturbed by children who made too much noise. If children had cause to go near that hollow, they had to pass around it very quietly indeed. They were told never to play loud games there in case this angry spirit was disturbed. If she was, she would become very annoyed and appear in a ghostly form; she would chant at the children:

> Ah'll put on my bonnet,
> And tie on my shoe,
> And if thoo's not off,
> Ah'll be after thoo!

In other words, if the children did not leave her in peace, she would chase them away.

Another old Flamborough story concerns the fisherman and the prior of Bridlington. It dates to the time of Edward III (1312–77) when the king gave to the prior the rights of fishery in the bay of Bridlington. This then meant that the prior could charge the local fishermen for the right to take fish from the bay and so he did. The charge was called the 'scist-fish'. On the day the fishermen paid their dues, however, it was part of the terms that the prior was obliged to give them each a flagon of ale and a sixpence. The skippers of the fishing-boats were allowed more ale than their crew-members, but in return they had to swear each year that they would maintain the tithe system.

This continued until some two centuries ago when one of the local men, John Ogle, decided to question the legality of this ancient tithe. He made enquiries locally but could find no foundation for it nor could he discover any reason why it should continue, especially as the annual payment to the church had increased until it was worth far more than a flagon of ale. Because he was unable to clarify the matter locally, John Ogle decided to travel to London to seek expert advice and, if possible, to get the tithe abolished.

But on the way he caught a severe fever and died before he could complete his journey. The sad fishermen of Flamborough therefore set off to London to recover his body and it was returned to Flamborough where it was buried with due ceremony. But his efforts were not in vain – the publicity he had generated resulted in the permanent abolition of the tithe.

8 Goodmanham
The Destruction of a Temple

The Wolds village of Goodmanham claims one of the earliest links with the establishment of Christianity in Britain. Its role in the history of the early church is well documented by no less a chronicler than the Venerable Bede himself. He includes it in his *History of the English Church and People* which he finished in AD 731. Although his book was written more than 1,260 years ago, it is a remarkable achievement and has been praised ever since for its scholarship and accuracy.

In Chapter 13 of Book II he relates momentous events which occurred at Goodmanham in AD 627, when the destruction of a pagan temple became part of our religious history and entered Wolds folklore. If the passage of time has dimmed the importance of that occasion, it can perhaps be put into perspective when it is learned that the destruction of that temple was one of the world's great historic moments. If that seems an overstatement, a study of the relationship between the events at Goodmanham and the subsequent course of Christianity in Britain will reveal its true impact, and will reveal Goodmanham's everlasting importance as a cradle of British Christianity.

But this is not a history book; it is a book of folk-tales and this story has come to us from the seventh century. Although it is part of our history, its repeated telling, often by word of mouth, surely qualifies it as a folk story. None the less, the events are true; they are no myth nor are they a legend, even if they have all the hallmarks of such.

Goodmanham is a pretty village which lies quite literally on the edge of the Yorkshire Wolds, little more than a mile from Market Weighton. It is a straggling red brick village with a mixture of old and new houses, a small inn and a somewhat squat but fascinating little church among yew-trees. The church has been much restored. The present building is Norman (*c.*1150), although the arch into the nave dates from the fourteenth century and the belfry was built in the fifteenth. The Normans used a west door for entry but that is now blocked and almost invisible, although the south door, still in use, also dates from Norman times. There are two more priests' doors in the chancel, both blocked, and there is a peep-hole in the chancel arch which gives a view of the altar. The font, dating from the fifteenth century, is large and stands almost five feet high, with rich carvings around its bowl.

Standing on the floor nearby is a much older and far humbler font. This dates from either Norman or perhaps Saxon times, but from some unknown date until 1805 it served as a horse trough. It was recognized by the vicar of Hotham who removed it to his garden, and it was eventually replaced within this church in about 1850. This old font is called Sax. Some accounts suggest it is even older than its probable Norman origins – for years, it was believed to be the very font which was used in the historic events of AD 627, but this legend has been discounted. Quite simply, the font is not that old but in any case, the famous baptism which features in the story was conducted at York, not Goodmanham.

The story concerns Edwin, the famous king of Northumbria. He was a pagan who worshipped Norse gods and idols, and his religious adviser was a high priest called Coifi. Edwin was a highly successful king and his strong but fair rule brought peace from coast to coast across the north of England. It was said that 'a woman and her babe might walk scatheless from sea to sea in Edwin's time.'

Among his achievements was to defeat the Picts and the Scots, to capture the Isle of Mona and change its name to Anglesey, and to found a city in Scotland called Edwin's Borough, now known as Edinburgh. He was eventually to rule almost the whole of England, with the exception of Kent.

In 625, however, Edwin decided to marry; his intended queen was a young princess from Kent. Her name was Ethelburga but unlike him, she was a Christian. She owed her faith to St Augustine, who had been sent to England by Pope Gregory the Great to convert the heathen English.

It was Ethelburga's father, King Ethelbert of Kent, who had welcomed the missionary priest and his band of monks to England in 597. Augustine became the first Archbishop of Canterbury. King Ethelbert was a pagan, but his wife was a Frankish princess and a Christian; she had ensured that the visitors were well-received. Ethelbert was a fair man who allowed his people freedom of worship and he soon abandoned his pagan faith to become a Christian.

He built a cathedral at Rochester and the first St Paul's Cathedral in London. Ethelbert is now honoured as St Ethelbert of Kent, with a feast-day on 25 February. It was the daughter of this fair, free-thinking man who trekked north to marry Edwin.

Ethelburga's chaplain was called Paulinus and he was a bishop, a member of the second band of missionaries to arrive in England from Rome. He arrived in 601, some four years after Augustine. His task was to be Ethelburga's spiritual guide and counsellor. One can only speculate upon the fears experienced by Paulinus as the royal party rode north to meet Edwin but Paulinus survived that ordeal and his simple goodness had a profound impact upon the king. Paulinus is now honoured as St Paulinus of York, with a feast-day on 10 October.

In a powerful man like Edwin, however, it was unusual to find such tolerance for the opinions of others. He was happy to listen to the teachings of Paulinus but steadfastly refused to embrace the Christian faith because he was afraid of offending his own pagan gods such as Woden and Thor. These gods, he explained to his wife and Paulinus, had enabled him to succeed as king and although he appreciated his wife's love of a Christian God, he maintained that he could not accept the faith she followed.

Then in 626, the king of the West Saxons sent an assassin to kill Edwin with a poisoned sword. By the time of that attempt, Edwin's chief minister, Lilla, had become a Christian and was at the king's side as the assassin struck. As the killer stepped forward, Lilla leapt between his sovereign and the sword. Edwin was so impressed by this act that he erected a cross to the memory of his martyred servant. Lilla Cross on Fylingdales Moor can still be seen and it is one of the nation's oldest Christian relics.

Edwin saw that Christianity had much to offer and allowed first his baby daughter and then eleven members of his household to be baptized. That occurred at Easter, 626, in a small wooden church in York – Edwin later decided to replace it with a building of stone which grew to become York Minster.

But while Edwin allowed his wife, his baby and members of his household to become Christians, he steadfastly refused to embrace the faith himself, even though he continued to express a deep interest in its teachings. He now decided it was time to defeat his enemies, especially those who had tried to assassinate him, and so, as a test, he asked his wife to pray to her God for victory. If her God was more powerful than his, then surely He would bring victory to Edwin? Ethelburg assured him that she would do as he asked. Edwin, in return, said that if he did achieve victory through Ethelburga's prayers to the Christian God, then he would consider acceptance of her faith.

Edwin did win those battles – he defeated no less than five enemy kings and a large number of others who had conspired to usurp him. His kingdom, and his life, was now safe. But it was no easy matter for a king of such power to abandon the faith in which he had matured. To do so demanded extraordinary courage and so Edwin decided to arrange a great Council of Northumbria to discuss the feasibility of his conversion. The agenda was simple – should the king, and therefore the kingdom, officially accept Christianity?

Among the wise men present at that meeting was Paulinus, his wife's confessor, and Coifi, Edwin's own adviser. The latter was now an ageing high priest who had resolutely followed the pagan faith and who had guided Edwin's career in that faith.

Coifi had erected pagan temples around the kingdom and one of them, a very important one, was located on a hilltop at Goodmanham, then known as Godmundinga-ham. It was decided that the venue for this important Council would be a royal palace close to Goodmanham, but the precise location is uncertain.

At that meeting, the king's friends, advisers and counsellors listened to the arguments for and against the new Christian faith. Paulinus spoke eloquently but briefly about his beliefs and the apostolic teachings, but it was Coifi, the pagan high priest, who set the meeting alight with his surprising views. His remarkable change of heart is recorded in the writings of the Venerable Bede. Coifi openly rejected the teachings of the religion that he had followed and recommended to others so faithfully through his life. He went on to say that no-one could have been more sincere or devoted to the pagan gods but that he now realized that his religion was worthless. He told the gathering that if the new faith was found to be better and more effectual, then none should hesitate to accept it.

This speech was followed by a poetic address from an old man who has not been named, other than that he was one of the king's chief men and a wise counsellor. From the Venerable Bede's record of the event, William Wordsworth produced these lines:

'Man's life is like a sparrow, mighty king!
That, stealing in, while by the fire you sit
Housed with rejoicing friends, is seen to flit
Safe from the storms, in comfort tarrying.
Here it did enter – there, on hasty wing
Flies out, and passes on from cold to cold;
But whence it came, we know not, nor behold
Whither it goes – e'en such that transient thing
The human soul; not utterly unknown
While in the body lodged, her warm abode –
But from what world she came, what woe or weal
On her departure waits, no tongue hath shown;
This mystery if the stranger can reveal,
His be a welcome cordially bestow'd!'

The other counsellors and wise men listened to his emotional speech, and then Coifi said he would like to hear more from Paulinus. Paulinus obliged and gave a longer account of the new faith which he had brought from Christ, through St Peter, the apostles and the Pope in Rome. When he had finished, Coifi's mind was made up. He had decided to abandon paganism and embrace Christianity.

It is difficult for us to appreciate the bravery of this man in making this announcement; here was the high priest of one ancient religion publicly rejecting it before the king to whom he had taught it, and then announcing he was to embrace a new faith brought from overseas. That took enormous courage but Coifi went further by adding that, in his opinion, all the existing pagan temples and altars should be destroyed.

The king agreed; this impressive conversion of a former leading pagan gave authority for Paulinus to preach the Christian faith throughout Edwin's vast kingdom, but Edwin then asked who would destroy the old altars, shrines and idols.

Coifi announced he would do it himself. He added that as the true God had now given him insight and wisdom, he would set an example to all pagans by destroying the very idols he had once worshipped in his ignorance.

He then asked for arms and a powerful stallion (it was not lawful until then for a high priest to carry arms or to ride anything but a mare), and set off to destroy the pagan temple.

A large crowd watched him ride away, some believing he had gone mad, but he galloped into Goodmanham and rode towards the pagan temple which occupied a hilltop. The crowds followed – surely, they reasoned, if Coifi destroyed the temple he had built to his gods, then those gods would now destroy him. They watched from a safe distance, fully expecting Coifi to be struck dead the moment he began his mad work. When he arrived, he threw his spear over the outer wall to embed it in the door as a gesture of his intent, and then, once inside the wooden building, began to systematically destroy all the evidence of his earlier faith. He smashed the altar, the idols and the shrine itself, reducing the entire building and its contents to splinters, and then, as a final act, he set the remains on fire.

The temple and its contents were destroyed – and Coifi was not struck dead. There was no retribution by the gods of old, there was nothing but a pall of rising smoke as the temple burned. The people now believed that Coifi was right in changing his faith, and the site of that pagan temple is now occupied by Goodmanham's little parish church.

Having witnessed this act, effectively the end of paganism as the official religion in Britain, Edwin now accepted Christianity. He was baptized in the church of St Peter which he had founded in York; his baptism was on 12 April AD 627, which was Easter Day.

With new authority for his teachings, Paulinus went on to baptize thousands of people in the north of England. He blessed the River Swale and in a letter to Pope Gregory, told how, on one day, he had baptized 10,000 people in it.

And so, through the actions of the brave Coifi, the pagan religion was rejected and Christianity came to the north of England. The tiny village of Goodmanham can boast its part in helping St Augustine to convert the pagan English.

9   The Gypsey Race
Waters of Woe

Among the enduring folk mysteries of the Yorkshire
Wolds, especially in the northern parts, is the cause of a
number of fast-rising streams known locally as 'gypsies'.
Another local term is Woe Waters because some believe
their appearance heralds national or local disasters.

They can be described as variable and intermittent
streams which appear on the surfaces of chalk valleys in
the Wolds; at times, they flow underground and
sometimes they disappear altogether, leaving little or no
evidence of their presence. They do appear in times of
heavy rainfall, and some older reports have indicated they
only make their appearance after such periods. Local
people, however, claim that their appearance is not
exclusive to such times; they can appear without warning
in dry weather too, when they can flow for a month or two
before ceasing as if by magic. Sometimes when they
vanish, they leave virtually no trace of their presence
because they flow through meadows where there is no
rocky river-bed of the kind associated with constantly
flowing water.

Their presence might be accounted for by this
explanation. When rain falls on the Yorkshire Wolds, the
water is very rapidly absorbed by the chalky, porous
surface and is apparently stored underground in vast
chambers. In addition, it seems that there are many miles
of subterranean passages where the water accumulates.
The inevitable result is that, from time to time, any surplus
water emerges like a spring to flow along the surface of
the ground. Although heavy rainfall will inevitably swell

these huge underground reservoirs to force an overflow, it is also possible that in fairly dry times, the water will gradually accumulate until some of it is forced to the surface. It will break through at well-established points, and so a gypsey stream can suddenly appear, even in dry weather.

Around the Wolds there are several places where such water emerges regularly to form sudden, fast-flowing streams. These streams do not always reach the sea or enter a river, but disappear underground as mysteriously as they appeared. It is possible that what on the surface appears to be a number of streams, may in fact be only one, with the water emerging and disappearing at different places along its route.

There is little doubt that our primitive ancestors believed that these springs came from a magic source, and some believed they were a goddess who appeared in this form. They considered that an unlimited, unexplained source of pure water was a gift from the gods. Primitive dwellers accredited the waters with healing powers and magical abilities.

By far the best-known of these Wolds streams is the Gypsey Race which, when flowing, makes a dramatic appearance near the village of Wold Newton. From Wold Newton, the Race flows ten miles or so to emerge in Bridlington Harbour, after passing through Burton Fleming, Rudston and Boynton. At times it can become a savage torrent of water up to twelve feet wide and three feet deep as it roars towards the North Sea. Sometimes the water emerges as fountains or geysers, and a fierce torrent will roar along the surface while yet other parts remain dry.

A glance at a map, however, will show that this stream appears to begin much further inland. It starts high on the Wolds above Duggleby not far from the medieval village of Wharram Percy.

There, it takes the form of a narrow ditch beside the road, and during a hot summer we noticed water in the ditch at Kirby Grindalyth, but the bed became dry as it approached Wold Newton. It seems to travel both over and under the ground as it flows onwards through West and East Lutton, Helperthorpe, Weaverthorpe, Butterwick and Foxholes, and then to Wold Newton where it passes close to Willey Howe, the prehistoric tumulus (see Wold Newton). From there, it follows the path already described to enter the North Sea at Bridlington.

The name has little or nothing to do with gypsies, although it is thought that gypsies did worship these waters. Quite possibly, it comes from an Old Norse source, 'geipsa' meaning to yawn or gape, and 'ras' meaning a rush of water.

But how reliable are these 'Woe Waters' as a means of forecasting doom?

Among the local and national disasters said to have followed the appearance of the Gypsey Race are the Great Plague of 1666, a great flood in 1860, a terrible storm in 1880, World War I, the General Strike of 1926, World War II and local floods in 1960. But the Race did not appear before the death of King George V in 1952 or of Winston Churchill in 1965 nor did it forecast either the Falklands or the Gulf Wars. It did appear in 1966, however, so perhaps it, or the goddess who controls it, is very selective as to what qualifies as a disaster?

10   Harpham
The Drumming Well

Harpham lies roughly half-way between Bridlington and Great Driffield, and is just off the busy A166 road. Kelk Beck flows nearby and the village is proud of one of its sons, St John of Beverley (see Beverley). This Saint John is patron of the village church and was born at Harpham in AD 640. He became a student at Canterbury and later entered the monastery at Whitby, where he was taught by St Hilda. In AD 687 he became Bishop of Hexham and in fact ordained the Venerable Bede into the priesthood. In 703, John was transferred to York as bishop, but resigned in 717 so that he could enjoy a peaceful retirement. He went to Beverley where he had earlier founded a religious house, and when he died there, it became a place of pilgrimage. The present Beverley Minster is the successor to John's early church, and his tomb is marked by a slab in the floor of the nave; he lies there with the rosary he used as a priest.

The villagers of Harpham are justifiably proud of their very own saint who was once revered throughout England as, in the words of Dame Julian of Norwich 'a dearworthy servant to God'. One of two wells in the village is dedicated to him and it was once claimed that miracles occurred to those who took its waters. The well, which was flowing when I called during the hot, dry summer of 1991, is surrounded by metal railings and bears a stone cupola (see Burton Agnes). The name 'St John's Well' is carved upon the stonework and the well stands beside a lane marked 'No Through Road'. There is also a

small pond nearby; this is along the low road to Burton
Agnes.

Another story was that a drink of this water could calm
the most ferocious of animals. One writer, William de
Malmesbury, said that it could cause dangerous bulls to
become as quiet as the gentlest lambs.

Harpham's second well has a less pleasant history
which involves another famous family of Harpham, the St
Quentins. They gave birth to one of the most enduring
folk stories from this part of Yorkshire.

In a field close to the church was a pond, known locally
as a well; this is the second well of Harpham, and it was
for years known as the Drumming Well. I could not find
this well or pond, and wondered if it once occupied the
depression in the field which now houses the tennis-
court.

But the story begins in the reign of Edward III (1327–77),
at a time when all the young men of England were
expected to become proficient archers. To encourage this,
regular contests were held, even in small villages.

Butts were built so that the archers could practise, and
field days encouraged them to compete. These field days
were rather like fairs. There were jousting tournaments,
archery contests, trials of strength and other skills as well
as music, food and dancing. People from a wide area came
to watch and it was a time when aristocrats and peasants
could mingle. The villagers were always pleased when
members of the St Quentin family attended to give their
support and encouragement. The squire of the time was
particularly keen that the village lads should become
highly skilled with the bow and arrow.

At that time, the manor-house stood in the field near the
church; between the well and the manor-house was a set
of training butts used for archery contests. One summer,
the village decided to stage one of its field days. The
arrangements were made and the entire village arrived to
watch, as did Squire St Quentin with his lady, and many
of their society friends. The squire wanted to show his
friends just how skilled and well-trained were the archers
of Harpham.

Among the spectators was a strange woman known as

Molly Hewson. She was a widow, and was reputed to have strange powers. People would often seek her advice or help. Molly had a fine son called Tom who was a clever, able lad, talented in many ways. The squire had recognized Tom's abilities and had appointed him trainer to the village archers. It was Tom's job to make sure they were trained to the very highest of standards so that they could defeat all comers.

Tom was also a talented drummer and so the squire had appointed him drummer to the archers; whenever they went to another town or village to compete in an archery contest, Tom would accompany them on his drums. Molly, and all the villagers, were very proud of him.

On the day in question, therefore, Tom was confident that his archers could defeat any of those from the neighbouring villages, and it was with some pride that Squire St Quentin settled down to watch the competitions. A large crowd had arrived and were excited at the prospect of some fine archery as the contest got under way. There was a certain tension in the air too, as the competitors strove to give of their best.

But one of the rustic farmlads was rather clumsy with his thick fingers. He began to struggle as he tried to fit his slender arrow to his bowstring, his huge, powerful hands being too heavy for such delicate work. As the crowd watched and laughed at his awkwardness, the squire became impatient; then some of the competitors began to chuckle at the lad's fumblings and this angered the squire.

He leapt from his seat and rushed across to chastise the youth but in his urgency collided with Tom Hewson who was standing near the well. Tom had his drum ready for the next piece of music and when the heavy squire collided with him, he fell backwards.

Within seconds, he was in the water. He was unable to swim because of the drum fastened to his chest and he sank into the deep, dark water. In the resulting pandemonium and panic everyone, including the squire, made a powerful effort to rescue poor Tom but none succeeded. He drowned in that well.

It took a while for Tom's body to be recovered but it was too late and there was no way that he could be resuscitated. Meanwhile, someone brought his mother, who arrived at the scene disbelieving the course of events. But when she saw the still form of her son, she threw herself upon his body and began to weep. The assembled people gathered around, too stunned to do anything. There were many tears for the popular Tom.

Then Molly stood up. She turned to face the distraught squire with her arms spread wide and her eyes bright with a curious glow. She remained immobile for several minutes, staring straight ahead as if in a trance, and then she spoke. It is said that her voice was almost sepulchral in tone as she exclaimed:

> Squire St Quentin. You were a friend of my boy, and would have still been his friend but for this calamity. You did not intend his death, but from your actions his death has come. Know then, that through all future ages, whenever a St Quentin, Lord of Harpham, is about to pass from this life, my poor boy shall beat his drum at the bottom of this fatal well. It is I, the wise woman, the seer of the future, that say it.

Tom was buried with due solemnity in the tiny churchyard. From that time forward, every time a member of the St Quentin family was on the verge of death, the ghostly drumming of Tom Hewson could be heard deep beneath the surface of that well.

A slight variation to this tale appears in some books.

It is said that William the Conqueror once fought a tremendous battle near Harpham, and on being victorious found himself in a very generous mood. He announced that he would give the entire village of Harpham to the first person to reach it. There was a race between many of his followers but the first person to arrive was a drummer-boy from the Conqueror's army. As he was about to enter the final stages, however, he was knocked into the well by a knight called St Quentin. St Quentin then claimed the village and so, whenever a member of that family was on the point of death, the ghostly drummer could be heard deep within the well.

11   Hornsea
The Battle of the Mere

Hornsea can be described either as a small coastal town or a large seaside village. The older part has some charming narrow streets and rather quaint cottages, while the sea-front has more to offer than neighbouring Withernsea (see Withernsea). Although the area is flat, there are extensive sea-views across Bridlington Bay and the town offers attractive gardens, a park and a handsome town hall with a museum of the town's ancient history. There is also a museum of North Holderness village life housed in old farm buildings.

Although it has very old origins, this former fishing village has become a busy and popular resort, especially for the people of Hull and West Yorkshire. It boasts a range of attractions other than the sea. There is, for example, a large pottery on the site of the defunct Brick and Tile Works with an added range of visitor interests such as gift-shops, refreshments, a model village, a picnic area and a zoo.

The splendid church is of interest too. Dating from the fourteenth century and built from stones found on the beach, it is dedicted to St Nicholas, the patron saint of sailors. It is noteworthy because the central portion was once removed and rebuilt without altering the exterior appearance. The church is very old, some parts dating from c.1220 and it was once covered by three steep-pitched roofs. Some believe it was similar to Cornish churches, especially its rubble-built aisles which date from the same period, the thirteenth century. The tower, built in the fourteenth century, lost its spire more than two hundred years ago, while the windows at the east end are of particular interest, if only for their huge size.

The remains of an ancient cross in the form of some steps and part of a shaft are in the south-west corner of the churchyard, albeit with a more modern decorative shaft now in place. This might be the remains of the old market-cross, although there is another old cross in Southgate near the cemetery.

The rebuilding of the central portion of the church, perhaps due to storm damage or even a fire, occurred in the fourteenth century and at the same time the chancel was lengthened. There is a curious brick crypt beneath the chancel; this crypt looks east and it is said to have been constructed to aid local smuggling enterprises!

There is a strange verse concerning this church which reads:

> Hornsea steeple, when I builded thee,
> Thou wert ten miles from Beverley,
> Ten miles from Burlington
> And ten miles from the sea.

Burlington is the old name for Bridlington (see Bridlington), but those distances bear little relationship to the modern map. Hornsea is now on the coast, Bridlington is thirteen miles away and Beverley is twelve miles away. While one can tolerate the errors relating to Bridlington and Beverley, it is most unlikely that Hornsea church was ever ten miles from the sea. Some believe this might have been an error and that the distance should really have been one mile. But it is of little consequence now because this old verse does, perhaps, serve to remind us that the sea is a constant threat to Hornsea and other communities along this coastline.

There is a lovely old story about the church and the smugglers who made use of its convenient crypt. It seems that the parish clerk, who was also a smuggler, was in the crypt on the day before Christmas Eve, 1732. He was checking the contents which he had stored there, perhaps with a view to making some profitable deals over the Christmas period, when a terrible storm broke out. As he worked among the huge stock of illicit goods, the storm intensified and rapidly became a severe hurricane. Trees were felled, house roofs blown off, millstones hurled for hundreds of yards and even a windmill was demolished. The busy clerk probably thought he was safe in that crypt, but then the roof of the church was blown off and its massive east window suddenly caved in with the force of the hurricane.

Tons of debris fell into the building, as a result of which the roof of the crypt collapsed. Suddenly the clerk was half-buried in rubble and masonry. The sheer terror of this caused him to have a severe fit which paralysed him; he was deprived of speech and spent the following months in bed, a wreck of a man. He died, still unable to speak or move, and the people of Hornsea saw this as an omen. They regarded it as the wrath of God upon a parish clerk who had sinned – and who had used church premises for his evil deeds. Never again was that crypt used for the storage of smuggled goods.

Of more urgent concern, however, was the constant action of the sea as it consumed the land to the seaward side of Hornsea. It worries people today, just as it worried the forecasters of last century; they said that the sea would, one day, reach the expanse of inland fresh water which lies behind the town, even if it appears to be a safe distance from the sea.

This large lake, rich with fish and wild-fowl, is an essential element of Hornsea's wide appeal. It is known as Hornsea Mere and is two miles long by almost a mile in width at its widest point. The distance around it is about five miles. It is the largest lake in Yorkshire and although purists might now say that it lies within the county of Humberside, traditionalists continue to assert that this part of England remains the East Riding of Yorkshire.

Various kinds of water-fowl inhabit the mere and most are now accustomed to human beings. They mingle with boats and cars on shore, sometimes coming to be fed with scraps, while ducks and geese snooze on the shore and refuse to move for passing people; one has to walk around them. The wilder forms of life here are subject to preservation, for this is a nature reserve, although fishing is allowed. The mere is also a focal point for boating and water sports.

There is an old folk story concerned with Hornsea Mere and it tells of an unholy and volatile dispute between two local abbots.

Shortly after the Norman Conquest, the town of Hornsea was given to the abbot of St Mary's in York, and he was therefore granted various rights in the town. He could impose tolls, charge fees for use of the market-place, create laws to govern the conduct of the people and levy charges on imported goods as well as on any ships which docked there. It seems that one abbot was particularly greedy. He enforced his powers with cruelty, even building a prison, a pillory and a gibbet with which to enforce his laws. He even charged tolls upon strangers passing through Hornsea and taxed food such as bread and ale.

It was obvious that such a man would wish to acquire all the fishing rights in Hornsea Mere. (For centuries, it has been renowned for the quality and quantity of its freshwater species, including pike, perch, eels, roach and tench.) The mere teemed with fish and the abbot of St Mary's therefore claimed that it belonged to his abbey. He was quite surprised, however, when a counter-claim was put forward. This came from William, the abbot of Meaux Abbey which was near Beverley and therefore much closer to the mere. William claimed that his abbey owned the fishing rights in some 500 acres of the southern half of the lake, but the York abbot claimed that he owned the lot. Thus there broke out the battle of Hornsea Mere (Hornsea was then known as Haraney, the name then meaning 'hare island').

As neither abbot would relinquish his claim, and the York abbot would not agree to share the fishing rights of the vast lake, it was decided that the only way to determine the matter was to organise a trial by combat.

This dispute raged sometime between 1249 and 1269, and records suggest that the fight probably occurred in 1260. Each abbot obtained the services of a worthy champion to fight on his behalf and the battle would be fought on the shores of Hornsea Mere. The winner would determine which of the abbots had the exclusive fishing rights to the disputed southern half of the mere.

On the appointed day, the two abbots with their champions and, quite probably, a band of supporters from each side, met on the shores of the mere. So that there would be no argument about which part of the lake was disputed, a horse was made to swim across the lake on the boundary line in question.

When it was retrieved at the distant side, all could identify the section which was the subject of the contest. Wooden stakes were hammered into the ground as a permanent reminder of the boundaries and so the battle began. There is no doubt that the two knights who fought for the abbeys were both superb with lance and sword, for their fight continued from early morning until late at night, with neither side being able to claim victory. But as time wore on, it became clear that the Meaux champion was weakening and in fact, he capitulated.

At this stage, the reports vary – some say that the abbot of St Mary's at York therefore claimed the disputed rights while others say that a compromise was agreed. It does seem, however, that although York won the contest and claimed the rights, they did allow their brothers from Meaux to fish there from time to time.

12   Keyingham
The Lovers' Well

Keyingham lies a short distance from the southern edge of the Yorkshire Wolds and straddles the A1033 which runs from Hull via Patrington to Withernsea. Known for its windmills, this small village occupies a low ridge which provides fine views across the flat landscape of South Holderness. In the distance to the south-east is the tall spire of Patrington's fourteenth-century parish church; this splendid building is famous throughout England for its grace and beauty. Known as the Queen of Holderness, the church is more like a cathedral than a village church and is well worth the extra drive from Keyingham. At Hedon, not far away, is another fine church; this is known as the King of Holderness. The King and Queen of Holderness stand some ten miles apart.

Keyingham also boasts a church, albeit of a more modest kind, and it forms one of a triple group of spires in this area – Keyingham has one, described as a plain broach spire which rises from the tower without a parapet; Patrington boasts the second and the third is nearby at Otteringham. This one was restored in 1860. The three spires have long served as guides for ships navigating the Humber, although the Keyingham spire suffered badly in a fierce storm of 24 June 1392. A thirty-foot section was demolished through a combination of lightning and gales, and all the oak doors inside the church were split.

A curious occurrence concerning one of the tombs is also recorded in the account of that storm. The tomb of Philip de Ingleberd, who was the parish priest of Keyingham from 1306 to 1325, was not harmed by the falling masonry which descended upon it, but was said to have oozed a mysterious sweet-scented oil at the time. Philip, it seems, was highly regarded when he was a student at Oxford, and during his later priesthood, many of the faithful regarded him as a saint.

Parts of Keyingham church date from Norman times and there is a medieval mass-dial on the wall. This is a type of sundial which featured on many parish churches prior to the Reformation; the moving shadow provided by the sun told the faithful when it was time to attend Holy Mass.

Parts of this old church (such as the font,) date from the thirteenth century, while the clerestory is from the fifteenth century and there are some interesting artefacts inside. Near the pulpit is an old hour-glass in its iron stand and there is a monument which is a reminder of local participation in the history of lighthouses. It commemorates John Angel, who died in 1647, whose family maintained a system of blazing beacons along the Humber for more than two centuries.

Keyingham is also known as the location of at least three ancient stone crosses.

One stood near an old farmhouse, another was in the churchyard and another faced the war memorial which bears the statue of a soldier. The cross in the churchyard is more than five hundred years old and is probably the one which used to be known as the Pilgrims' Cross. During pilgrimages, the faithful would halt at certain crosses along their route so that mass could be said, refreshments taken and a short rest enjoyed. This is one of those halting places.

At the time, there was a well near the Pilgrims' Cross and there is no doubt that this provided a nourishing supply of fresh water for the pilgrims. The well became known as St Philip's Well, and in bygone times, the cross was also known as St Philip's Cross. Whether the saint in question was the local priest, Philip de Ingleberd, or the apostle Philip, or one of the other saints of this name, is uncertain.

Whoever its patron, the well was highly-regarded by the local people and especially so by the fair maidens of the village. Some believed that fairies dwelt at the bottom of the well, others thought it contained holy water while yet more thought it had special magical qualities. Lots of wells or springs were attributed with supernatural powers because the supply of water never ceased, and it was so pure that the users thought it cured ailments. The truth is that it didn't cure ailments – it simply didn't cause them!

Thus the water of St Philip's Well was considered mystical in a variety of ways and it was this which attracted the young ladies of Keyingham and district. In their case, they believed that romantic fairies occupied the well, and that if you made the fairies happy they would ensure that you were rewarded with a handsome husband and that you would live happily ever after.

No one is quite sure of the origin of this particular aspect of the mystique of this well but it could have started with a fair maid called Thomasina. She was desperately in love with a handsome youth called Guy de Halsham who lived nearby. Guy was a dashing young cavalier and a superb horseman; he was proficient with the sword and came from a wealthy family. Thus he was regarded as a fine marriage candidate and many of the local maids dreamt of being betrothed to him.

It was Thomasina who succeeded. She did so by smiling seductively at Guy as he rode through Keyingham one fine afternoon in July. The sun was beating down and he was hot and thirsty, so he halted at the side of the beautiful girl.

When she saw his condition, she suggested he take a drink from St Philip's Well.

'If you will accompany me to the well,' she smiled at him. 'I will draw the water for you.'

Dismounting from his fine white charger, Guy accompanied her to the side of the well and they both peered into the dark water below. The well possessed a fine stone canopy under which a long rope supported a wooden pail, but before Thomasina lowered this into the water, she pointed to the pool below. their images were reflected in the shining surface, almost like a mirror, for there was not a ripple on the cool calm water.

At that moment, Thomasina tossed in a silver coin. It

splashed, shattering their reflections and then, with the sunlight glinting from it, sank and was gradually absorbed by the mysterious depths of the water. Slowly the water became still once more and their calm reflections were again visible.

'Why did you throw that coin into the well?' asked Guy. 'It was silver, silver is valuable.'

'It is for the fairies,' she told him. 'We reward them for looking after us, or we give them silver if we desire a wish to be granted.'

'So you have made a wish?' he smiled.

'I have,' she said, blushing deeply, and at that moment Guy knew he was in love with Thomasina. They walked together all that afternoon and ate strawberries in the sunshine. Before long, they were married and lived happily ever after.

13 Kirkham
The Foundation of a Priory

The remains of Kirkham Priory lie deep in a quiet, wooded valley on the north-western edge of the Wolds between York and Malton. They are less than a mile from the busy A64 York–Malton road and the easiest way to find them is to leave the A64 at Whitwell-on-the-Hill and follow the signs, while being alert to the steep hills and sharp corners of these country roads.

Although, in its prime, the church was one of the most beautiful in this country, the ruins are modest, especially when compared with nearby attractions like Rievaulx or Byland Abbeys. None the less, Kirkham's splendid and unusual entrance is dramatic. Access to the old priory is through a surviving, but ruined gate-house, which is one of the finest in Yorkshire or even the whole of Britain. The gate-house was probably constructed between 1150 and 1200, much of it being rebuilt in Tadcaster stone and later remodelled, but the stonework is remarkable for the number of heraldic shields and carved figures which still adorn it.

There are ten shields which represent families who have been associated with the priory, perhaps through marriage, as patrons or in some other way. The families represented by the shields are the following: top row, left to right – de Clare, Plantagenet, Ros, Vaux; centre L'Espec, Greystoke or FitzRalph; bottom row – Scrope, Ros (again), Ros (again) and de Fortibus.

One of the shields is believed to commemorate the marriage of Sir Henry Scrope with Margaret, daughter of Lord Ros, while another reminds us of the marriage between Gilbert de Clare, Earl of Gloucester and Hertford, and Joan Plantagenet, daughter of Edward I, in 1290. The figures are of Christ and some of his saints, one headless figure possibly representing Philip and another being either Bartholomew or Barnabas. The carvings depict two of our best-known battles, the fights between St George and the dragon, and between David and Goliath, although some accounts suggest one of the fights may have been between a member of the Ros family and a Scottish foe. Empty spaces show where several statues were removed during the Reformation, including one known to have depicted the Crucifixion and another the Virgin Mary.

The gateway is said to be unusual in monastic terms because it led into the cloister, and also because it was wide enough to admit carts which would normally have had a separate entrance. Another interesting feature is the priory's lavatorium with six hand-basins, said to be the loveliest surviving example of its kind in Britain. This is where the monks washed their hands before taking their meals and its geometric design is said to be 'sheer perfection'.

Kirkham is a priory, not an abbey. It was governed by a prior, who is of lesser rank than an abbot, and building began in 1121. Of its many buildings, the church was planned as early as 1130 and grew from a small building to one over three hundred feet long, almost the length of Beverley Minster. Today, the riverside-remains reveal the massive outline and some relics of this former splendid structure. Many of the visible remains date from the Norman period, including a superb doorway into the refectory. The church tower stood until 1784, when it was demolished in a gale.

In spite of its beauty and splendid setting, Kirkham Priory never achieved the stature of the famous abbeys nearby like Whitby, Fountains or Rievaulx, nor was it involved in many of the great events of English history, although the priory was regularly modernized and extended between the twelfth and fourteenth centuries. At its Dissolution in 1539, when Henry VIII sought to eliminate the Catholic Church from England, it had only seventeen inmates, an indication of its minor status.

Today the ruins are open to the public and the priory's beautiful pastoral setting forms the perfect background for a stroll beside the placid River Derwent which curves through the hills as it flows gently past. The name 'kirk-ham' means church-meadow and even now, the wooded hills and calm rolling meadows provide a haven of peace and solitude, while the view from the bridge which spans the river near the priory is truly delightful. The only regular noise is the roar of a nearby weir.

One surprising element is the proximity of a railway line – although there is no village of Kirkham, save for a scattering of houses, the valley does provide the route for the busy railway between York and Scarborough via Malton. As a consequence, passengers can get a fine view of the priory ruins as they pass, while the former Kirkham Station is now a garden centre and coffee-house. The signal-cabin continues to function however, and from it the level-crossing gates are operated. A fine stone-built inn, The Stone Trough, stands on a hillside above the priory, so there are points of interest in addition to the priory ruins.

Until the last century a curious custom took place on Kirkham bridge. It was known as the Kirkham Bird Fair and seems to have been a wonderful excuse for young men to meet young women late at night! At two o'clock in the morning of the Monday following Trinity Sunday, youngsters from the district would meet on the bridge to sell, barter or exchange their pet birds, which included starlings, jackdaws and larks. This exchanging of birds continued until the sun rose, and as Trinity Sunday follows Whit Sunday, it therefore falls upon a late spring date. For those attending the bird fair, it meant that sunrise would be in the very early hours of the morning, probably around four or five o'clock. When the exchange of birds was over and day began at this early hour, there was a long session of drinking, eating, music and dancing which continued until the sun set on that same Monday evening. It was a mammoth party and there is little doubt it led to many romances and marriages. Although the bird fair is known to have started some eight hundred years ago, its precise origins and purpose are obscure.

In looking upon these quiet remains in such a peaceful setting, a visitor may be prompted to ask – why was such a splendid priory built in such a remote spot? The answer lies in a folk story concerning a noted landowner of the time, Walter L'Espec, who possessed huge tracts of land in northern England. L'Espec was one of the most powerful barons in the north and led the British to victory against the Scots at the Battle of the Standard at Northallerton in 1138. He became renowned throughout the nation and amassed considerable wealth and power, with several homes and many servants.

Walter had a fine wife called Adeline and a young son, also called Walter, who was an active youth interested in hunting, archery, horsemanship and all country pursuits. Walter and Adeline took care to teach him the many responsibilities of a baron in twelfth-century England. In the future, young Walter would inherit the vast estates of his father and he would then be responsible for running them with efficiency and care. The L'Especs were exceedingly proud of their son and although they lavished great love upon him, he was not spoilt. His father knew better than to encourage the youth to be idle and indolent, and consequently he had to work hard to meet the high standards demanded by his devoted parents.

Walter would probably have been around thirteen or fourteen years old when tragedy came to the L'Especs. One morning in 1120, Adeline had a premonition that something would go wrong that day; she had no idea what it might be, but she did experience a tremendous sense of foreboding and decided that she ought to persuade young Walter not to go hunting. He had told her of his intentions – there was some fine sport to be had in the woods and meadows of East Yorkshire and he was looking forward to a great day of action in the open air. But Adeline warned him not to go.

'I fear for you, my son,' she said. 'Please do not go today. Another day might be better, there is plenty of time to go hunting...'

'Mother,' he said with all the confidence of youth. 'I am one of the most skilled huntsmen in this region; I was taught by my able father and I am a very experienced horseman too. No harm will come to me, I assure you; please do not try to prevent me doing what I must. I am a man, mother, and must behave like one. But I will take care.'

Adeline failed to persuade young Walter to abandon that day's hunting and, with tears in her eyes watched him ride from their manor. He was a fine youth, mounted on a superb and spirited horse, said to be the speediest in the county, but her heart was heavy with sorrow.

By all accounts, the day was very successful and although young Walter never experienced any hurt or fall from his horse, he was always aware of his mother's warning. But the day passed without incident and Walter bade farewell to his friends for the final ride home. It was a fine evening with the sun setting behind the hills to the west, and Walter was singing as he rode the final half-mile home. Ahead lay his parents' fine house where he knew his mother would be waiting anxiously, perhaps with a meal ready, and he could then tell her about his exciting day. He could also deliver the fine deer he'd caught – it was now being carried home by two bearers and he could give it to his mother as a gift. They could celebrate later with a splendid meal of finest venison.

As he emerged from a clearing in the forest, he saw a long open route ahead and so he spurred his horse into a fast gallop. With the wind in his hair, he shouted with glee as the thrill of the gallop coursed through his young body. Over the final yards, Walter had to descend a steep slope which led towards the river, but as his horse sped down the hill there was a fearsome noise. A wild boar, terrified by the shouting youth and the galloping horse, burst from the thick vegetation and darted right in front of Walter's sweating horse.

The horse could not avoid it. Whinnying in alarm, it reared high onto its hind legs before stumbling across the panic-stricken boar. And young Walter fell from the saddle.

In normal circumstances, he would have survived such a tumble, but as he fell, his foot caught in the stirrup and he was dragged along the ground. As the startled horse galloped out of control, the boy's unprotected head was smashed against the base of an old stone cross which stood beside the lane. It was an awful collision. A youth who was fishing nearby witnessed the event and ran to help Walter, but it was too late. He had died instantly from a fractured skull.

The unfortunate witness now had the awful task of breaking the news to Adeline and her husband. They were overwhelmed with grief and for a long time felt unable to cope with their tragic loss. Both were inconsolable and eventually Walter decided to seek advice.

A cousin, William L'Espec, was the parish priest of Garton-on-the-Wolds, and Walter took Adeline to visit him to ask for his spiritual help in coming to terms with their loss. William listened with sympathy to the sad story and then suggested that, as a perpetual memorial to young Walter, they should establish a church at the site of his death. Walter decided to do that – but not only would he build one church, he would build three.

In memory of his son, therefore, Walter L'Espec founded the splendid priory at Kirkham, constructed virtually upon the spot where his son died, and two more religious houses, one at Wordon in Bedfordshire and the other at Rievaulx in the North York Moors.

But just outside the famous gate-house of Kirkham Priory there are the substantial remains of an old cross. The large square base is complete, but the cross section is missing. It is said that this is the very cross which brought about the tragic death of young Walter L'Espec.

There is a further legend attached to Kirkham Priory. It is known as the Curse of Kirkham. Apparently, when the priory was demolished following the Reformation, the stones were taken away by a local family who constructed a manor-house from them. It is said that true happiness would never come to that family or their successors.

This might be the legend associated with Howsham Hall which is near the banks of the river Derwent, only some three miles from Kirkham. This Elizabethan mansion was constructed in Howsham Park and it is said that the family which built it, the Bamburghs, used stones, timber and other materials taken from the ruins of Kirkham Priory. This was considered sacrilege at the time and so a curse was placed upon the house and its owners. That curse said that all male heirs of the estate would perish, and in fact the Bamburgh family did die out through lack of male heirs. Their successors, the Wentworths, intermarried with the Bamburghs through the female line, but that family also became extinct. The next owners, the Cholmleys, also failed to rid themselves of the curse and the family became extinct.

Howshall Hall is now a preparatory school.

14   Langtoft
Great Floods and a Fire

Langtoft's place among the folk-tales of the Wolds arises from two massive floods which devastated this quiet village. Its situation deep in a narrow chalk valley has often led to its being flooded by water from the surrounding hills, but two of these floods were exceptional and terrifying.

Langtoft, like so many Wolds villages, is most charming in its sheltered position among the rolling hills. The surrounding area has revealed many relics of prehistoric times, some in the form of earthworks or entrenchments, and evidence of Roman occupation has been discovered nearby. One historian counted 197 earthworks in the area, including one known as Danes' Graves, which is a misnomer. It probably contained the bodies of people who inhabited this part of Yorkshire more than 2,000 years ago, long before the Danes.

In the thirteenth century, Langtoft produced a famous poet and writer, Piers of Langtoft. He became a monk at Bridlington Priory and was the author of an early history of England, beginning with the ancient Britons and ending in the time of Edward I. Another of his achievements was to collect folk-songs sung in his time; some are still sung today, more than 700 years after his death.

Until recently, Langtoft had two village ponds; however these have both been filled in. The war memorial stands near one, and the other is a short distance from a handsome cross on the top of three steps. The shaft of the latter contains the carved image of a saint, while eight carved panels depict rural scenes. This was given to the village by Sir Tatton Sykes of Sledmere; similar monuments donated by the Sykes family can be seen in other parts of the Wolds, Sledmere included.

Another of Sir Tatton's beneficial works was to restore churches across the Wolds, and between 1900 and 1903 he turned his attention to the ancient parish church of St Peter at Langtoft. It is a large building, set among trees on the slope of a hill overlooking the village and boasts a particularly fine chancel dating to the fourteenth century. Some portions date from 1150, while much of it comes from the thirteenth century, including two pillars in the south arcade. Two fourteenth-century windows were re-set by Sir Tatton. The church has three fonts, one of which is still in use and has a stunning suspended cover.

Set in a busy farming area, the village is in two sections, separated by rising ground. Its cottages, some a mixture of brick and chalk, are charming, and many have red pantile roofs. One of them, in the centre of the village near the Ship Inn, bears a plaque which commemorates the two great floods.

The first occurred on 16 April 1657 but there is little detail of precisely what happened, except that the village was said to have been half-submerged. The height of that flood is unknown.

More information survives about the second great flood. This occurred on Sunday 3 July 1892, when more than seven-and-a-half feet of water roared through Langtoft following a terrific thunderstorm. Another cottage bears a plaque to this flood, showing the water's height upon the outer wall.

The morning of that Sunday was hot and cloudless but as the day wore on, the breeze dropped and the air grew perfectly still. The atmosphere became oppressive and a heavy copper-coloured sky brooded over the surrounding countryside. Gradually, this developed into menacing black clouds of ominous colour and weight, and as evening approached they began to move towards Langtoft. As they reached the hill above the village, there was a tremendous crack of thunder and lightning streaked across the sky. The clouds seemed to spiral down towards the ground in swirling columns. Then their peaks broke, and as one account says, a huge volume of water was unleashed upon the hillside.

At the place where this cloudburst hit the ground, a series of deep rents were torn into the grass- and chalk-covering of the hillside, more reminiscent of an earthquake than a downpour, and then a huge torrent of water rushed down the hill, creating great fissures in the ground. Those marks provided dramatic evidence of the sheer power of that collossal flow of water. It raged through the village and swept away houses and walls, haystacks and farm buildings, gates, hedges and livestock.

The people fled. Then, as the water devastated their village, an almighty hailstorm broke out. All the time, thunder rumbled around the hills and lightning flashed across the black sky. It was a storm of unbelievable severity.

Fortunately, and surprisingly, no human lives were lost, but the story of that awful day has been passed down by word of mouth through generations of families who lived in Langtoft. The hills above the village still bear the scars of that terrible day and the Ship Inn has a collection of photographs taken just after the flood.

Another frightening event in Langtoft was a severe house fire. It occurred in the fourteenth century and features one of the amazing miracles of St John of Bridlington (see Bridlington). According to legend, the fire broke out in the upper room of a cottage in the middle of Langtoft. It was during the night hours but the crackle of the flames and the screams of the householder roused the entire village. Neighbours rushed to the house, but the fire was so fierce that it had trapped a woman in the upstairs rooms.

She was screaming for help as the fire raged about her and a young man rushed into some outbuildings and returned with a ladder. Hurriedly he placed it against the wall, only to discover that it was far too short to reach the window where she stood, rigid with fear. The man called for a longer ladder and the distraught villagers searched frantically for one, but to no avail. Suddenly one of the villagers cried out that the answer was to pray to St John of Bridlington and so they all sank to their knees in prayer. Instantly it was found that the short ladder had miraculously doubled its length. The young man climbed to the window and managed to rescue the terrified woman just before the thatched roof collapsed and the entire house was consumed by the flames.

15 Rudston
The Rudston Pillar

Rudston is one of East Yorkshire's most historic villages. It contains the remains of a Roman house, while part of a mosaic Roman pavement was found along its Kilham Road in 1933. It is now in Hull Transport and Archaeology Museum. There is a Norman church and a pretty old school-house with a bell-tower. Rudston is also the birthplace of the novelist Winifred Holtby who wrote *South Riding*. In addition, it is the home of the tallest standing-stone in England, the famous Rudston Pillar.

The sprawling village lies just off the old Roman route between Bridlington and York, and now sits astride the B1253 which runs from Bridlington towards Sledmere. The village's main street follows the route of a prehistoric track and nearby lies a group of four round barrows. Another group can be found a short distance to the east, and they mark the burial-sites of Neolithic and Bronze Age people. Originally there were seven of these mounds and two were excavated in 1869. Led by a Canon Greenwell, the examination revealed the bodies of numerous men, women and children, along with bronze and flint implements. Some of the bodies were protected by planks of willow-wood on either side of the corpses, but not fastened together to form coffins. Arrows were also found and one interesting discovery was a food-urn with four lugs or ears on it, the exterior being decorated with the imprints of a tool or implement of some kind.

Two Iron Age cemeteries have also been discovered to the north of Rudston and experts believe the village was a focal point for religious activity during the prehistoric period and at all times since. It is believed that Rudston has been a sacred place for some 4,000 years, first as a pagan centre and then as a focus of Christianity.

Various other artefacts from Rudston's past have been unearthed. In 1933, for example, the ruins of the Roman house were discovered nearby during ploughing. It was seen to have had central heating, tessellated floors, a wide gateway and a range of beautiful rooms. Some had been decorated with sea-creatures like dolphins and oysters while another contained a portrait of the goddess Venus. Fragments of pottery, jewels, and builders' materials were also found, including some small brick-like blocks which were thought to have been prepared for construction of a floor.

On its hilltop site, the church of All Saints and its grounds are of immense interest. Restored in 1861, it has a Norman tower with walls four feet thick, a Norman arch leading to the nave, thirteenth-century arcades leading to the aisles and an interesting organ-screen. The chancel is over 600 years old and there are many surviving items of Norman stonework, including a blocked doorway.

Among the memorials inside are those to the famous Constable family. One is a brass inscription to Sir William Constable who died in 1527, but the memorial to his wife, Jayne, is incomplete because the blanks for the date of her death have never been filled in. In fact, she died in 1540.

The graveyard contains the burial-places of the MacDonalds of the Isles, as well as the interesting tomb of a local boy, Alistair John Thompson, who died in 1955 aged 10. His grave is marked by a life-size statue of him.

Winifred Holtby, the prize-winning novelist who was born in Rudston on 23 June 1898, is also buried here. Her grave is next to the plot marked 'The Burying Place of MacDonald of the Isles'. There is a memorial to her in the church, but her grave is marked by an open book fashioned from marble, which bears these words:

> God give me work till my life shall end,
> And life till my work is done.

But the churchyard contains another object of immense interest and speculation; the huge grey standing-stone known as the Rudston Pillar, which gave the village its name. Rudston comes from the Old English 'rood' or 'rode' meaning cross, and 'stan' or 'stane' meaning stone. This suggests that at some early date this massive monolith might have had a cross-shaped head. In many cases, both in this country and overseas, crosses were added to the tops of similar standing-stones in an attempt to replace their ancient pagan associations with the new Christianity. Thus 'rood stane' could mean Stone of the Holy Cross but that name must date only from the beginning of the Christian era. We do not know its name before that time.

As happened elsewhere, this renaming could have been an attempt to give Christian credence to an object previously used for pagan worship or ceremonial, for both this stone and the church were even then known to occupy a site which has enjoyed important religious significance since prehistoric times. Some argue that the pillar may have been a central feature in ancient sun-worship or that it might have represented some other pagan deity; it might even be simply a monument to some ancient god.

Throughout its long history, the pillar has become weathered by the effects of rain, sunshine, wind and the other elements, while its name has periodically changed until it has become known as the rudston. This, in turn, is now the name currently enjoyed by the whole community while the stone itself is identified by words such as monolith, pillar or merely the Rudston Stone. The Rudston Pillar, as I shall call it, stands some 25 feet 9 inches out of the earth in spite of the fact that a piece is probably missing from the top – it might even have been as high as 28 feet. In the late eighteenth century, a type of lead cap covered the tip to protect it from the weather. This was later removed, but has since been replaced.

It is claimed that the stone descends a further 25 feet into the ground; this was determined by the late Sir William Strickland around 1795 when he conducted a survey of the stone. It is more than 5 feet 6 inches wide at its widest point near the ground and over 2 feet thick. It has been hewn from rock, as its squarish shape will reveal, and it narrows slightly towards the top. Estimates of its weight vary between 28 and 80 tons! It is fashioned from a type of stone not found in this part of Yorkshire. The nearest source is at Cayton near Scarborough, about ten miles away.

The stone is thought to have been erected during the Neolithic period or perhaps the Bronze Age, probably as a religious symbol. This means it is several thousand years old; it was known to be old when the Romans and the Normans occupied the surrounding countryside, so if it was erected for religious purposes, how was it moved from the Cayton area, and how was it carved into this distinctive shape?

There are two folk stories which purport to give the answer.

A very old legend says the stone fell out of the sky. It was regarded as a sign of the wrath of God because, so the story said, the huge stone killed several people who were in the act of desecrating the churchyard. There is a possibility that this tale dates to the very earliest days of Christianity. In those times, preachers of the new faith warned of the dangers of following the older creeds by linking those outlawed religions to the machinations of the devil. Their teaching was that any religion other than Christianity was surely the work of Satan! Thus they ensured the new Christians refrained from worshipping around the old stone by making them frightened of it, the supposed desecrators of the churchyard no doubt being members of the abandoned pagan faiths who had come there to do mischief.

The other legend, which applies to similar stones, such as those known as the Three Arrows at Boroughbridge in North Yorkshire, is that the Rudston Pillar arrived here through the work of the devil. For many centuries, so the legend says, the devil had attempted to win the people of Rudston but his efforts were always thwarted, especially so when the church was built. The villagers abandoned the devil for the hope represented by the new God. In his frustration and anger, the devil decided to destroy

Rudston church and for this he used one of his legendary arrows, which was in the form of a huge stone missile. He unleashed it at the village church, but his aim was not very good – he missed!

The huge arrow came to rest in the earth beside the church and the building survived that onslaught. Thus the devil was thwarted and Christianity survived.

This was clearly a warning which dates to the beginning of Christianity, the teachers trying to show in this way the lengths to which the devil would go to destroy the new faith. It also perpetuated the association between the devil and the old pagan beliefs – new believers were taught that if the stone was originally used for pagan worship, then its presence was surely the work of the devil in his efforts to destroy Christianity.

16   Skipsea
A Murder and a Mystery?

Skipsea is some seven miles south of Bridlington and several miles east of the rolling hills of the Wolds. It is one of several Holderness villages which have, throughout their history, been threatened by the ever-encroaching North Sea. Quite literally, the sea comes closer with each passing year. Today, the waves are less than a mile from the village.

In the time of William the Conqueror, Skipsea was a place of considerable stature but it is now a quiet village with visitors usually passing through *en route* to either Bridlington or Hornsea; however, some do make the effort to stay locally and to explore the coastline. There are some interesting old cottages here, particularly those built of pebbles from the beach. I spotted an old house called Cobble Garth whose outbuildings reveal the picturesque use of those beach-pebbles. They are a direct contrast to the many chalk-built cottages which feature along this coast. To the west of the thirteenth-century pebble-built church, which was restored in 1866, there are some large earthworks which serve as a reminder of Skipsea's former glory.

One, known as Albermarle Hill, is probably a natural mound but was the site of an important castle. The man who built the castle was called Drogo de Beurere or Brevere, who was described in the *Chronicle of Meaux Abbey* as a Flemish adventurer. He fought alongside William the Conqueror at the Battle of Hastings in 1066 and was honoured by the Conqueror by being allowed to marry one of the king's nieces. His greatest honour,

however, was to be granted the Seignory of Holderness by
William.

Thus Drogo became the Lord of Holderness, a huge
tract of flat land which spreads along the coastline, and he
decided to build his castle at Skipsea. He selected the
hilltop site to the west of the present church where it
seems there was probably a stronghold before Drogo's
time. He built a fine motte-and-bailey castle of wood, with
a wooden bridge over the moat. It was to this place, a
splendid building in its time, that Drogo brought his new
bride.

But tragedy came to this Lady of Holderness. She was
killed by her husband, but history does not acquaint us
with the means of her death, nor does it enlighten us as to
whether her death was an accident or murder. We do not
know whether she was stabbed, beaten, drowned or
poisoned – the only note occurs in a contemporary record
which says she was killed 'omine infausto'. A local version
is that she was poisoned by Drogo who blamed her for his
dwindling fortunes, somehow coming to believe that she
was a sorceress. He persuaded her to drink from a
poisoned chalice and secretly buried her body near the
castle.

But afterwards, Drogo was haunted by the ghost of a
White Lady who appeared with a golden chalice in her
hands, just like the one he had handed to his wife, saying
it contained a love potion. This terrified him and alarmed
the servants who were already suspicious about the
sudden disappearance of their gentle and holy mistress.
They began to discuss it among themselves and then the
villagers heard about it.

Drogo became fearful of the Conqueror's reaction
should he hear the news and decided to conceal her death
from the king. He hurried to meet William and asked to
borrow money by using the pretext that he wanted to
return temporarily to Flanders and take his wife with him.
He said she was homesick and would benefit from a short
time in her homelands. It seems that William believed the
story and gave the necessary sum of money to Drogo, who
lost no time in escaping overseas – but left his dead wife
behind.

With Drogo away, the servants began to search for their mistress and soon discovered her dead body. They raised the alarm; the Conqueror was notified with all speed and was furious at the deception. He sent his constables to arrest Drogo and they checked all his known haunts and escape routes. But it was too late. The crafty Drogo had escaped and was never seen again.

His vast lands in Holderness were confiscated and William then gave them to a new lord called Odo. He was also the Lord of Albemarle, a son of the Count of Champagne and husband of another of the Conqueror's nieces, called Adeliza. But Odo did not appreciate this gift – he complained to William that the land was barren, except for oats, and so the king also gave him Bytham in Lincolnshire so that Odo could bring up his own son on wheaten bread. The Seignory of Holderness continued within the hands of the House of Albemarle until the reign of Edward I (1272–1307) when it reverted to the Crown, due to a lack of male heirs. The castle, however, appears to have disappeared before this time – one of the earls of Albermarle, William de Fortibus, rebelled against King Henry III (1216–72) and the king's response was simple. In 1220, he ordered the destruction of Skipsea Castle.

But this is not the only historic drama to occur in Skipsea. Evidence of another was to be found in a field near the earthworks where the castle had once stood. This evidence was in the form of four large bare patches of earth where it was said the grass would never grow. The reason for these barren patches was a duel which was fought for the hand of a fair maiden. The folk account of this battle does not inform us of its date, although some believe it occurred during the Danish occupation of the seventh century, while others suggest it happened in a later period.

Some say it was a duel between two Danish soldiers for the hand of a local maiden. One tale is that both soldiers were killed and the woman committed suicide. The truth is that we do not know the name of the lady in question, nor the identity of her two suitors, nor even the outcome of that event. What we do know, however, is that something terrible happened at this place which, for

centuries afterwards, bore an aura of gloom and mystery.
Even now, it is said that the White Lady continues to
haunt the area of the former castle, sometimes appearing
during daylight hours, and the villagers do tend to avoid
Drogo's hill during the hours of darkness.

Following those events, so the story tells us, no grass
would grow on the land. It remained barren, apart from a
few paltry weeds and for centuries afterwards, it was the
custom of local farmworkers to clear the weeds and other
rubbish. This was done every Michaelmas Day (29
September) by the lads who worked at Castle Farm.
Michaelmas was the time when farm-hands attended the
annual Hiring Fairs in the hope of being offered work by
the farmers who went there. The lads of Castle Farm
believed they would not be offered work if they failed to
tend the patch of land.

It is odd that such a small place, and indeed that one
tiny piece of land, should contain one ghost and two folk
dramas involving death and a lady.

I did wonder if, through the passage of time, the facts of
Drogo's attack upon his wife have become so blurred and
indistinct that the story of her death has been transformed
into the story of a mysterious duel over an unknown
woman.

17 Stamford Bridge
Seven Feet of English Soil

In their history lessons, schoolchildren have been taught about two famous battles which occurred in 1066. One was at Hastings but the first was at Stamford Bridge in the East Riding of Yorkshire.

The Battle of Stamford Bridge is memorable because of a phrase which has crept into our folklore. When King Harold of England was at Stamford Bridge preparing to do battle against Earl Tostig and King Harald Hardrada of Norway, he was asked by Tostig what he would give Harald as the price of withdrawal.

'Seven feet of English soil', he is supposed to have replied, 'Or as much more as he may be taller than other men!'

The story of that great battle, inevitably associated with that famous retort, is now part of the region's folklore but it includes a second story which has also entered our folk history. There are several versions of this battle, none of which is accepted as totally reliable and so the following account is adapted from several sources.

But first, a look at Stamford Bridge itself.

It is an attractive village just beyond the western extremities of the Yorkshire Wolds and is a mere seven miles or so from York city centre. It is a busy place which draws many visitors but it is able to cope with them and their demands. There are some nice restaurants and inns, and the inevitable reminders of its permanent role in English history.

The village straddles the A166 which leads to Bridlington via Great Driffield, and there is a narrow bridge built in 1727 which is controlled by traffic-lights. Wide enough for only one vehicle at a time, it carries the main road across the lovely River Derwent. This is not the original bridge from which the village gets its name – that was a short distance upstream. That ancient bridge, whose position may still be pointed out by the local people, became crucial to the outcome of the 1066 battle. Later, another old bridge was constructed of wood and it stood at the same place on a series of stepping-stones in the river-bed. It was those stepping-stones which gave the village its name – 'stane ford' (stone ford). Stone ford has since been corrupted to Stamford, with the suffix 'Bridge' added to distinguish it from Stamford in Lincolnshire. Some authorities have suggested that Stamford Bridge was formerly the site of a great Roman fort known as Derventio, although others favour Malton as its location.

The road into Stamford Bridge from the Wolds above Fridaythorpe was formerly a Roman highway, and nearby is Aldby Park which was once thought to be an important Roman villa. In the eighteenth century, Aldby was famous for another legend – here was born, in 1715, a racehorse called Flying Childers, said to be the finest ever bred. A chestnut with a white nose and four white legs, it was never beaten in its racing career. The legendary horse died in 1741.

The river at Stamford Bridge, with its impressive weir, dark pools and former mill, was once the boundary between the North and East Ridings of Yorkshire. Today, it continues to serve as a boundary, this time between the administrative counties of North Yorkshire and Humberside, created in 1974. It was this boundary, with an old wooden bridge as the link between the two Ridings, which formed the battlefield of the historic fight at Stamford Bridge. Although there is now little visual evidence of the actual battlefield, names like Battle Flats and Dane's Garth survive.

The story begins with the death of Edward the Confessor, who was king of England from 1042 until 1066. He acknowledged Harold, the son of Earl Godwin of Wessex, as rightful heir to the throne and so in 1066, at the age of 44, Harold found himself king of England. He inherited the throne just as severe trouble loomed from overseas – already he knew of an impending invasion, somewhere along the south coast, of a massive Norman army led by William of Normandy. Harold spent the summer of 1066 watching the south coast – and waiting.

But there was worse to come. While he was in the south, another army of invaders, this time from Denmark and Norway, had entered the River Humber and was sailing towards York.

The army comprised some 60,000 soldiers in 500 ships and was led by King Harald III of Norway, known as Harald Hardrada. Accompanying the invaders was the treacherous Earl of Northumbria, called Tostig. He was, in fact, brother to King Harold of England and felt he should have had the throne. He set out to gain it, if necessary by killing his brother, and so this unlikely alliance was determined to conquer the north of England.

In the north, however, King Harold had two brothers-in-law called Edwin and Morcar and they discovered that the Scandinavians were camped at Riccall, some ten miles south of York. In support of Harold, they set off to meet, and hopefully repel, the invaders but had only reached Fulford, on the edge of York, when they were confronted by the well-organized invading army. There was a fierce and bloody battle in which Edwin and Morcar were totally defeated; the victorious Scandinavians marched into York and the frightened, defenceless citizens handed the city over to them.

When Harold heard of this, he abandoned his watch on the south coast and forcibly marched his army to Yorkshire. It was an incredible feat of speed and endurance, and Hardrada had no idea that Harold was *en route*. Harold surprised the Scandinavians, many of whom had returned to their camp at Riccall but who were drunk and disorganized after their easy victory and conquest of York. They were in no mood to fight and fled in disarray, but Harold followed and eventually caught up with them. Thus the two armies found themselves facing each other at the place now called Stamford Bridge.

The date was Monday 25 September 1066. Before Harold's arrival, however, Haralda Hardrada had managed to establish his troops in Stamford, and his army straddled the river, being massed along both banks. The bulk of his army was on the eastern bank, ie inside the East Riding of Yorkshire, while he had left some outposts and a vanguard on the western bank.

The old wooden bridge separated them, but when Harold arrived on the scene at seven o'clock in the morning, he caught the outposts and vanguard by surprise. But before battle could commence, Tostig and Haralda Hardrada were roused and the leaders confronted one another. Harold addressed his brother, Tostig.

'If you keep the peace,' he said, 'I will offer you part of my kingdom, Northumbria, or if this is not sufficient, I will give you a third of my kingdom.'

'And what will you offer my friend, Harald Hardrada?' asked Tostig.

'Seven feet of English soil,' retorted Harold. 'Or as much as he may be taller than other men!'

As the Norwegian king could expect nothing more than a grave from Harold, there was no need for further discussion or compromise, and so battle began.

From a few minutes after seven o'clock that morning, the armies fought along the North Riding bank of the river. The English had managed to dispose of the outposts and vanguard, who were unprepared for this early-morning attack, but they then had to face the massed Danes and Norwegians on the other side of the River Derwent. Already, some had managed to cross the bridge, but the English had driven them back. There was little doubt that the English were superior, but they could not completely cross that bridge to dispose of the remaining soldiers because of the actions of one huge Norwegian warrior.

This man, whose name is not known, has also entered our folklore annals because he held that bridge, single-handed, against the English army. Wielding a massive axe, he stood in the centre of the narrow wooden bridge and took on all comers. The English archers tried to dislodge him, but failed to do so; it is said that although he was struck many times by the bowmen, none of the arrows penetrated his thick armour. When English soldiers were sent to fight him hand-to-hand they were killed by his mighty axe, and it is claimed that he slaughtered at least fifty in this way.

The giant Norwegian had unlimited reserves of strength; he seemed invincible, until a bright English soldier had an idea. As the attention of the huge warrior was focused on the succession of Englishmen who attempted to get past him, the lone soldier found a wooden pig swill tub, climbed into it and let it sail down the river.

Armed with a spear and a sword, he guided his makeshift boat under the bridge and then, as the Norwegian warrior was engaged in battle with yet more Englishmen, the soldier thrust his spear up between the gaps in the wooden planks of the bridge and into the soft underparts of the giant. As he fell, more thrusts from the sword destroyed this magnificent fellow and so the English were able to swarm across the bridge to continue their battle.

By now, the river and the narrow bridge was littered with the corpses of the dead. It is said that the English soldiers had to walk across the bodies of their fallen comrades in order to gain the other side, but this they did and promptly set about conquering the remainder of Harald Hardrada's army.

Thousands of men died in that battle. Each side lost huge numbers and their bodies lay unburied for weeks afterwards. Among them were the corpses of Harald Hardrada, King of Norway, in its shining helmet and brilliant blue cloak, and the remains of the treacherous English nobleman, Tostig of Northumbria. It is said that Tostig was killed by his own brother, King Harold, who used Tostig's own sword for the task. Another story is that Harald Hardrada was buried where he fell, somewhere on Battle Flats, but his grave was never marked.

Harold's victory was total; the defeated Norwegians fled and it needed only 20 ships to take away the remains of the army which had required 500 to bring them to York. Harold began to celebrate but even as he did so, news reached him that William of Normandy was about to land at Pevensey in Kent with another huge army of invasion.

Harold was then faced with another long, rapid march to the south. He gathered troops along the way and so, for the second time within a month, King Harold found himself fighting invaders.

The famous Battle of Hastings began at 9 a.m. on 14 October 1066. One of the tactics employed by William was to shoot arrows into the air so that they dropped onto the opposition. One of them entered Harold's eye to end his short but very active reign. William then began his famous Conquest and earned himself the nickname of William the Conqueror.

In Stamford Bridge, the local people continue to relate the story of the gallant victory of King Harold, and of the daring deed by his unknown soldier. The scene is depicted on the sign of a local pub, The Swordsman. For years afterwards, that event was celebrated at Stamford Feast which was held on 25 September, the date of the battle. A huge pie, and later lots of small pies, were made in the shape of that makeshift boat and eaten in commemoration of the brave Englishman. That custom ceased in the early years of this century, but enjoyed a revival in the mid-1960s.

18 Watton
The Legend and Miracles of Watton Priory

Watton is a tiny village between Market Weighton and
Beverley. Watton Beck flows past before joining the River
Hull and so quiet is the district that it seems almost as if
history has ignored it. But it has suffered from past
violence and a reminder survives in what has become
known as the legend of Watton Priory.

In fact, there are several stories, one of which gives an
account of a miracle, but some writers have merged two
tales of violence into one, for both involve the savage
death of a woman. One was a nun and the other was a
lady of the manor, and their deaths occurred during two
different historical eras.

The brick-built village straddles the A164, with the
church at one side of the road and most of the village at
the other. To find the church, follow the signs to Watton
Carrs, but even then it is possible to miss it, for it is
well-concealed behind a row of trees. A small bridge
crosses Watton Beck from the lane to the church. The
church is unusual in that it is built of Tudor brick and not
the stone which has been used for most other churches of
its kind. It has a Norman arch, and some parts date from
the thirteenth century; the font is about 700 years old. I
liked the sign on the door which asked visitors to close it
to stop birds flying in.

Years ago, there was also a Gilbertine priory at Watton,
located not far from the church. Some grassy mounds, the
reminders of a past excavation, mark the site, but little else
now remains.

The priory stood on the site of an eighth-century

nunnery which had been destroyed by the invading Danes. It accommodated both monks and nuns and had two churches, two central cloisters and a high arcade designed to separate the monks from the nuns. Nuns considerably outnumbered monks and their premises were considered the more important of the two. The priory was surrounded by a moat upon which it was possible to sail a boat, and it enclosed about twenty acres of land.

After the priory was destroyed on 9 December 1539, on the orders of Henry VIII during his Reformation, some of its stones were used to build a superb Elizabethan private house with turrets, which stands near the church. Some accounts say it occupies the site of the prior's lodging. Its interior is reminiscent of a church or abbey; walnut trees planted by the abbot were incorporated into the house-gardens, and the priory's former fish-pond is now known as Fishpond Field. The house is in private hands and is not open to the public.

Parts of the original convent became the stables of the house and there was once a hollow square to remind us of the location and size of the kitchen. For a long time, the whole premises continued to be surrounded by the moat. The present stream is thought to have formed part of that moat, although it is rather too small to permit boating on it. The convent was also noted for its 'olde dinying chamber'.

In the seventeenth century, however, the only surviving stones from the priory were taken away and used to repair Beverley Minster. It is sad, therefore, that there are so few remains of what was England's largest Gilbertine priory. In some accounts it is misnamed as Watton Abbey – the correct title is Watton Priory. An abbey was governed by an abbot while a priory was under the control of a prior, a rank lesser than that of abbot.

It is possible that the early convent, built around AD 718, was the Vetadun mentioned by the Venerable Bede; he told of a visit by St John of Beverley (see Harpham), when the saint miraculously cured a girl called Quoenburg whose arm had been poisoned. This is one of the recorded miracles of Watton Priory.

Quoenburg was the natural daughter of the prioress and it seems that St John, during his retirement at Beverley, was a regular visitor to the priory where he gave spiritual guidance to the nuns. He became a friend of the prioress, called Heribury, and it was she who asked him to examine the girl's injured arm.

The prioress specifically wanted John to touch the girl's arm, so she invited the old priest to dinner. Before eating, he examined the girl. Her arm was badly swollen, so much so that it would not bend at the elbow, and it was bleeding. John laid hands on the injured arm as requested, prayed over the girl and blessed her. Then he went down to join Heribury for dinner. Minutes later, a servant dashed into the room to say that Quoenburg had been cured – the swelling had gone and the girl was free from pain. She could move her arm as if it had never been injured and there was no sign of her earlier torment. As Quoenburg said, 'As soon as the bishop had said the prayers and given me his blessing, I immediately began to mend. Although I have not yet recovered all my former strength the pain is quite gone from my arm and all my body as if the bishop had carried it away with him.'

This was recorded as a miracle of the time.

The second recorded miracle of Watton Priory involves a sad story of violence, lust and revenge.

In the twelfth century, a small girl lived in the convent at Watton. She had been placed there by Archbishop Murdac of York who was then living in Beverley, but the purpose of this is not given. It was, however, a fairly common practice for young girls to be placed in convents with a view to them becoming nuns in later life. She might have been a relative of Murdac, perhaps a niece placed in his care.

The little girl was called Elfleda and was described as a merry, vivacious child, and a source of pleasure and amusement for the nuns. Even those who were bad-tempered and lacking in humour found the little girl quite charming; she had a delightful laugh and indulged herself in childish games about the premises. It was a pleasure to have her in the convent, but as she grew older it became evident that her behaviour was not quite the

sort that was expected from a future nun. Her
conversation was cheeky, her humour likewise and she
indulged in many outbursts of bawdy language and
laughter.

In addition, she was becoming a very beautiful young
woman. One old account says that her form 'gradually
developed into a most symmetrical figure and her features
became the perfection of beauty, set off with a transparent
delicacy of complexion such as would have rendered her a
centre of attraction even among the beauties of the Royal
Court.'

The snag was that Elfleda's beauty made the other nuns
jealous. They lacked her beauty, they lacked her cheerful
nature and they lacked her open sense of humour. Many
were very ugly and others were so devoted to a narrow
interpretation of their faith that they regarded Elfleda's
behaviour as contrary to that expected in a convent. Most
of them were elderly women or at the least, late
middle-aged.

They began to treat the lovely girl with scorn, ignoring
her when moving about the building and conducting acts
of petty spite and persecution upon her. When she
retaliated, they charged her with entertaining ungodly
sentiments, with being a rebel, with rejecting God and
with favouring the devil and all his works. They forced her
to do many penances and other corrective actions and
although she was strong enough to withstand these
taunts, she did wonder what kind of life lay beyond the
dreary walls of the convent which had become more like a
prison.

It was part of the charter of endowment of Watton
convent that its routine management (as opposed to its
spiritual work) was undertaken by lay brethren, both men
and women. They would come from the surrounding
villages for discussions with the prioress about matters
such as money, food, maintenance of the buildings and
other routine concerns. Elfleda saw these people coming
and going and began to watch for them, listening to their
chatter and desperately wishing to become acquainted
with them and their worldly knowledge.

In particular, there was one young man who made

regular visits to discuss repairs to the stonework and roof. He was a charming young man, very polished and confident, with lovely eyes and a most engaging way of speaking.

Elfleda found herself growing very excited whenever he arrived and soon he noticed her; they began to exchange glances and she found that her heart was pounding each time he gazed upon her. They could never talk because the other sisters were all around, keeping a watchful eye on the giddy Elfleda; indeed, some had already noticed the rapport between the young couple.

But somehow the youth made it known to Elfleda that he would like to meet her outside the walls; with his talents, he could arrange for a secret opening in the wall and so he and Elfleda began to meet under cover of darkness. She would creep out at night and they would walk, talk and make love in the serene countryside around Watton. And the inevitable happened; Elfleda became pregnant. After a time she could not conceal her condition, and as an old account says, 'suspicion having been excited by her altered form', she was called before her superiors to explain the matter. The open, honest Elfleda admitted everything.

She added that she now knew she had no vocation as a nun and asked that she be banished from the community. But the old sisters would have none of this – Elfleda had brought disgrace to the convent, they said, and for that she would be punished. They considered a range of suitable penalties – should the girl be burnt to death? Should she be walled alive within the convent? Should she be flayed with whips until the flesh fell from her bones? Should they tear her flesh away with red-hot pincers? They could roast her to death, or hang her or drown her...

The sisters decided to be lenient. They stripped her naked, stretched her upon the stone floor of her cell and scourged her in turns until the blood ran down her back and trickled across the dirty floor. She was then thrown into a windowless dungeon and secured to the floor with iron hoops with only bread and water for sustenance. This was brought to her by nuns who teased, tormented and castigated the girl in her misery.

They managed to coax from the poor girl the name of the

father of her child, and that he would soon secretly visit her; he would announce his arrival by throwing a stone onto the roof of her cell. The nuns asked the neighbouring monks to lie in wait and seize the visitor; they did so and brought him into the convent. The nuns wanted to take control and the monks agreed; it seems they said they wished to find out more about him and his actions with Elfleda. But when they got him, they treated him atrociously.

An account says, 'On taking him to an unfrequented part of the convent, they committed on his person such brutal atrocities as cannot be translated without polluting the page on which they are written, and to increase the horror, the lady was brought forth to be witness of the abominable scene.'

We are not told whether the youth survived his ordeal, but Elfleda was returned to her cell and fastened to the floor. She then had a vision of Archbishop Murdac; she blamed him for incarcerating her in this place, but he answered that she should curse herself for having given way to temptation. She apologized and was forgiven – then the apparition vanished.

Later, she had another vision – two women came to visit her and then the Archbishop, but in fact these were not visions, they were real, for she had given birth to her child, which was taken from her. When the nuns came next morning, they accused Elfleda of having murdered her baby, a preposterous accustion, for she was chained to the floor. Although she told of the two women and the Archbishop, no one would believe her. Next morning, however, the nuns had a surprise.

Every one of Elfleda's shackles had come away during the night and there was no sign of them. She was standing in her cell, quite free and looking in perfect health, with no signs of either having just given birth or having endured such an ordeal. This astonishing development puzzled the nuns and even frightened them, and they called in their Father Superior who, having heard the story, asked for the assistance of the noted Abbot of Rievaulx, Aelred. He was later to be canonized as St Aelred.

Aelred conducted an investigation and concluded that

something miraculous had occurred in that cell.

As he wrote, 'Let no one doubt the truth of this account. I was an eye-witness to many of the facts and the remainder were related to me by persons of such mature age and distinguished piety that I cannot doubt the accuracy of the statement.'

This story, therefore, became known as another of the miracles of Watton Priory, and it is still told in that context.

The third story, however, is no miracle. It is a haunting, and although hauntings are not a feature of this small collection of stories, I have included it to complete the tales from this remote East Riding priory.

The house which was built on the site of Watton Priory is said to contain a secret priest hole. In the Penal Times when it was regarded as treason to be a Catholic priest, many large houses had hiding-places constructed within their walls. These were used by priests to avoid capture by the authorities, and there is no doubt that many owed their life to those members of the aristocracy who continued to support the old religion in this and many other ways. The hiding-place at Watton was in a chamber wainscoted throughout with panelled oak, one panel of which formed a door. It was so cleverly disguised that it could not be distinguished from the other panels and was opened by a secret spring. Inside was a stone staircase which led eventually to the outside of the premises, close to the moat.

The room which contained that secret door was said to be haunted by the ghost of a bloodstained, headless lady who carried a baby in her arms. It has been seen by several visitors, some of whom knew nothing about its reputed presence. It was said that if a visitor used the room, the ghost would appear and stand motionless at the foot of the bed, and then disappear. One man who witnessed this said she bore a remarkable resemblance to a lady whose portrait hung in the same room – so on that occasion, she must have been wearing her head! On some occasions, when no one was using the room, the bedclothes would be turned back as if someone had made use of the bed.

The story of the haunting begins in the time of the Civil War. The lady of the house, whose name is not given, was a supporter of the Royalist cause and a devout Catholic. She was also the mother of a small child.

A band of fanatical Puritan soldiers were on the rampage in Yorkshire and word reached the Lady of Watton that they had reached Driffield, only about five miles away. There they had plundered, raped and killed the local people, one of their sports being to throw babies into the air and catch them on the points of their pikes. As her husband and many of the villagers were away fighting for the king, she had no one to protect her save a handful of aged servants, and she felt certain the soldiers would head for Watton.

They vowed to put all Catholics to the sword, and they swore to kill anyone who supported the Royalist cause, so she had real cause for alarm. Her only recourse was prayer. She ordered that the massive front door of the house be secured, then locked herself in the room with the secret panel, fearful for her child rather than herself, but reasoning that if they did reach the door, she might escape through the secret panel. The soldiers arrived as anticipated and upon being refused admittance, began to examine the exterior of the huge house. They found a stone archway near the moat and some of them entered, finding themselves climbing a steep staircase until they came to a panel. They realized it was a concealed door and smashed it down – to find the lady inside the room, cowering on the floor with her child, her rosary in her hands.

Bravely she demanded an explanation and they said they had come for the man of the house, whom they described as The Egyptian. She refused to give them any information; they said they would tear the house apart, steal her plate and jewellery and kill her and her infant unless she co-operated. But she refused. One of them gave orders to 'Hew down the woman of Belial and the spawn of the malignant'.

And so the baby was killed by having its head dashed against the walls, and the lady was decapitated – then they rode off with the spoils of their raid.

From that time, it is said, the room has been haunted by the spectre of the headless lady.

There is one delightful tale about this haunting. In 1780, the house was occupied by a Mr Bethell and one night he was giving a candlelit dinner-party for some friends. The dining-room adjoined the haunted chamber and as they ate in the shadows of that place, they heard a scratching sound coming from it. As this was late in the evening they had been discussing the ghost and they were all terrified, but they assembled some group courage and decided to examine the room. As they entered with their candles, they realized the noise came from beneath the floorboards and so called in the estate carpenter.

He took up the boards and found an otter with her cubs – she had somehow found her way from the moat, up the secret staircase and into a space beneath the floorboards!

In spite of that simple explanation for a puzzling noise in a haunted room, Watton Priory is still said to have a ghost.

19   Withernsea
The Sisters Who Could Not Agree

Withernsea is the setting for a folk story which is repeated in many towns and villages throughout Britain. No one can be sure of the setting of the original tale, and in Withernsea's case, any possible evidence has been washed away by the sea.

As the name suggests, Withernsea stands on the coast and is literally on the edge of the sea, so much so that much of the older town has been washed away. The coastline of a thousand years ago was a mile further out to sea than the present one, and the district is rich with stories of vanished homes and buildings. Entire villages have been washed into the North Sea along this coastline and the ceaseless action of the waves continues to create problems for coastal dwellers.

Even the lighthouse at Withernsea is different from most because it does not stand on the coastline – it is in the middle of the town, about a quarter of a mile from the shore, and stands at the junction of the roads to Hull and Hornsea. It has occupied this site for almost a century, being built in 1893 and first coming into operation on 1 February 1894. It is one of only two in the country to be kept by a man-and-wife team – the other is at Lowestoft.

Withernsea's name is locally pronounced with a curious rolling 'r' and it has become a holiday resort for the people of Hull, to whom it is reasonably accessible. In 1854, a special railway line was opened between Hull and Withernsea and it enjoyed a brief period of busy use, but it was closed following the Beeching recommendations of the 1960s. A pier was built too, but a large ship which was being tossed about by a storm demolished it in 1880. When it was rebuilt, a raging gale swept it away two years later. No one seems to have tried since to build a new one.

Withernsea's position on the long promontory which terminates in Spurn Point means that it is somewhat isolated from the rest of Britain. Although it has a pleasant and attractive beach, Withernsea has not become a major resort, possibly due to the bleakness of its situation and the unappealing flatness of the surrounding countryside. Stiff breezes from the sea are a continuing feature – one even lifted the roof off the fifteenth-century church in the seventeenth century, and the entire town bears evidence of its continued exposure to storms and salty sea-air which is described hereabouts as 'bracing'. It does not claim to be a beautiful town nor does it boast any handsome buildings; in fact, most travel writers and topographical authors are unkind to Withernsea and its surroundings. One described it as a 'dull little watering place which was ragged and ugly to look at'.

Another said it was 'an absolutely dreary and dismal collection of lodging houses and shops, planted on a flat land which has scarcely a feature of relief in its entire prospect.'

I would not be so hard upon the place, but if Withernsea lacks beauty, it does have a long history even if very little evidence remains. This is undoubtedly because its older buildings have all been consumed by the sea. The church stood in ruins for years, probably after its roof had been torn off in storms around 1600, but it was restored in the years before 1867, some would say not very handsomely. It is one of the oldest buildings in Withernsea; evidence of this is shown on a stone in the porch which bears the date 1491 and an inscription to the memory of a man called William Copland. But this was not Withernsea's first church – an earlier one was swept away by the sea and erected further inland, but that replacement was also swept away. It seems that the present building, erected in the fifteenth century, is probably the third church – and even that has been radically altered and bears evidence of its long suffering from the elements.

It is those two vanished churches which have given rise

to a folk story, but even this is lacking in details such as names or a definitive historical period.

The story is that, in medieval times, two wealthy sisters decided to donate a church to Withernsea. But when the time came to decide upon its appearance, they argued bitterly. One wanted a tower while the other demanded a tapering spire. Neither would accept the plans of the other and so they decided to build two churches, one with a tower and the other with a spire. At great expense, this was done. One church stood very close to the coastline while the other was further inland. For a few years, these fine buildings survived the ravages of the sea and the wind. When the sisters died, each was buried within the graveyard of her 'own' church.

But as time passed the sea continued its encroachment of the shoreline and eventually the church nearest to the coast vanished into the waves, and with it went the grave of the sister who had built it. Nothing remained; not a single stone survived. The second church did remain for a while but the ever-approaching waves eventually overwhelmed it too. It was washed away in the course of a single night during a ferocious storm, but it left a solitary grave. It was the grave of the remaining sister and it survived until the last century, the only reminder of that sisterly argument. But in 1816, so the story goes, there was a further awesome storm and it was finally washed into the North Sea, leaving nothing but this story behind.

20   Wold Newton
A Visit From Outer Space

Wold Newton is known for two natural phenomena – it is on the route of the famous Gypsey Race (see Gypsey Race) and is also known as the village where a strange thing fell from heaven in 1795.

A small, open and sprawling village built on an old Anglian settlement among a network of country lanes, Wold Newton is some ten miles inland from Bridlington, ten miles south of Scarborough and six from Filey. There are several old burial-mounds around the village, including Willey Howe, the largest in this area. It is 24 feet high and 120 feet across the base and is the focus of a folk story in the chapter on Burton Fleming.

Wold Newton has a pond on the village green, so typical of the Wolds, which in this case it is called the Mere. Some of the village houses and barns are built from the distinctive white chalk which has been quarried nearby, while others are red brick, some being painted white to give the village a picture-postcard appeal. The small church of All Saints dates from the twelfth century and contains some Norman relics such as the font, a doorway, a window and an archway. The Methodist chapel is now a community centre and there is also an old pinfold, the alternative name for a cattle pound.

While the following tale can scarcely be classified as a genuine folk story, it is worthy of inclusion in a volume of this kind, because accounts of the event continue to be passed on by word of mouth. Such accounts are often exaggerated and others omit salient facts such as the date.

I was given an account of this event only three days before settling down to compile this volume, thus indicating that the tale is still very much of interest to those who know and love the modern Wolds. It is therefore fair to say that the story of the thing from outer space has become Wold Newton's own folk story and that it will continue to be told in years to come.

The story begins on Sunday 13 December 1795. The weather was typical of the time of year – it was a grey, miserable day with low cloud, drizzle, some outbursts of rain and even rumbles of distant thunder and flashes of lightning. At three o'clock in the afternoon it was growing dark, but the weather and the onset of darkness had not deterred some people from being out of doors. One of them was called John Shipley, a farm worker, another was a shepherd whose name is not given, and two were sons of the vicar of Wold Newton.

We have been left with an account of their experience through the foresight of a Mr Edward Topham who lived at Wold Cottage, on the outskirts of the village. He made a written record of the occurrence. Mr Topham was the son of a noted Prerogative Court judge of the time, Judge Francis Topham and was himself a magistrate. He also ran a farming enterprise from his cottage, employing the shepherd and the farm worker who feature in this story. They were returning from work at the time.

The first indication of a dramatic event was a whistling or screaming sound in the sky. Several people heard it and then noticed a white-hot object which was hurtling inland from the sea and travelling in a north-westerly direction. It was witnessed by several people in other villages, but no one knew what it might be. As it came towards Wold Newton, it began to fall from the sky, making directly for Edward Topham's cottage.

Fortunately it missed the house but fell two fields distant, some 150 yards away, with a tremendous explosion. As Topham wrote, 'The explosion really alarmed the surrounding country and created so distinctly the sensation that something very singular had happened.' John Shipley, the farm worker, was so close to the scene that he was hit by flying mud and earth as the missile embedded itself in the ground, but we are not told whether he was injured in any way. The force of its impact drove it through a foot of earth and into seven inches of solid chalk, at the same time creating a hole more than a yard in diameter.

The vicar's two sons ran to Mr Topham's house to inform him and to seek advice, for Topham was considered a man of wisdom and decision, and he went to inspect it. He described it as a stone; he would call it a meteorite. It was so firmly embedded in the ground that it required several people to dig it out, after which it was carried to his home. He weighed it and found that it weighed 56 lbs. He also measured it and said it was thirty-six inches long and twenty-eight inches broad. It was described as having a black and vitrified surface exhibiting marks of volcanic origin, or at the least of having been, by some means, exposed to the action of fire. The inside was white and of a granulated but very compact nature, but it was totally different from any kind of stone that had yet been discovered on earth.

Edward Topham, practised in the recording of legal evidence, took written statements, on oath, from all the witnesses and later wrote an account which was published in a work on British mineralogy.

Meanwhile, the metoerite was taken to London for exhibition in the Natural History Museum.

So that future generations would remember the incident, Topham erected a brick-built monument to record the event. Weather-beaten, it stands about three-quarters of a mile from the village centre, off Rainsburgh Lane which leads towards Thwing, and is on the exact spot upon which the meteorite fell. The inscription reads:

Here
On this spot, Dec 13th, 1795
Fell from the atmosphere
An extraordinary stone,
In breadth twenty-eight inches,
In length thirty-six inches
and
Whose weight was fifty-six pounds.

This column
In memory of it
was erected by
EDWARD TOPHAM,
1799

21 A Wolds Inn
Up Stick and At 'Em

Once upon a time, there was a remote inn high on the Yorkshire Wolds. It vanished a long, long time ago, although if you are lucky, you might still find evidence of its presence in the form of some old walls, floors and a derelict cellar. A good area to search, so we are told, is the countryside around Huggate.

Nearby there lived a youth called Jack whose father was very cruel; he made Jack work far too hard and beat him frequently, so much so that Jack decided to leave home. But Jack was in love with a lovely Wolds lass called Jill. His father would not let him marry Jill – he said Jack could marry her when he was rich, but his father never gave him any money ...

Jack loved Jill so much that he had no wish to make her poor by marrying her without money of his own and so, before leaving to seek his fortune, he promised that one day he would return as a rich man and marry her. Jill said she would wait. As Jack crept away one night, he realized he had nothing of his own, no money and no belongings save the clothes he was wearing, but he was utterly determined to make a life of his own. He trudged across the Wolds and eventually came upon a lonely farm.

He thought he might rest for the night in a barn and perhaps find a turnip upon which to feed, but when he entered the yard, he saw a very old man. He asked him if he might spend the night in a barn. The old man said he could use a bed in the house if he wished and then added, 'I am very old and need help. If you will work for me, I will provide you with food and a bed ...'

Jack decided that this would provide him with a chance to rest and eat and accepted. He stayed several weeks, helping the old man to work the farm, repair the buildings and care for his livestock. Then Jack knew it was time to leave and on the morning of his departure, the old man said,

'Jack, you have helped me enormously and I am grateful. I have no money to pay you any wages, but I will give you this donkey instead.'

'Thank you.' Jack was very grateful for he could sell the donkey if necessary.

'Listen,' said the man. 'I am old and shall not live much longer. I have no family and as you have been kind to me, I can tell you that this is a magic donkey. If you need money, all you have to do is to pull the donkey's right ear until he shouts, and coins will fall from his mouth.'

Jack did not know whether to believe this, but thanked the old man and left to continue his travels, now riding the donkey. He was able to earn a few shillings here and there by working on farms and doing odd jobs.

Eventually he came to an inn high on the Wolds where he decided to rest. He would use some of his money to pay for a fine meal and a comfortable bed, and would stable his donkey. But the landlord was mean and greedy and wanted Jack to pay in advance – and the cost was more than Jack had earned.

'Wait a second,' said Jack. 'I will return with enough money in just a moment.'

Jack thought he would test the old man's story about the donkey – if it was not true, he could always ride away. When Jack went outside, the landlord thought he had a secret bag of coins hidden somewhere and watched him carefully, but was amazed to see Jack pull the donkey's ears. As it hee-hawed in pain, a flood of money fell from its jaws. Jack was astonished – so the story was true! He went inside and paid the landlord, who decided he would make Jack the finest meal he had ever eaten while allowing the donkey to rest in the stable. That would make the lad fall fast asleep …

As Jack slept soundly, the wicked landlord crept out to the stable and swopped the donkey for one of his own which looked exactly the same. Overnight, Jack had dreamt of Jill and now realized he had all the money he could ever want. He would go home, tell his father he had made his fortune, and then marry Jill. Next morning, he mounted the donkey and never suspected that it was not his own.

When he arrived home he said to his father, 'Father, I am now a rich man and wish to marry Jill.'

'Show me your money,' said his father.

But when Jack pulled the donkey's ears, nothing happened; no money tumbled from its jaws. Jack tried and tried again as the poor animal cried in pain, but it yielded no money. When he went back to his father to say he could not produce evidence of any money, his father seized a hayfork and walloped him soundly, beating him until he was black and blue while calling him a wastrel and a liar.

Jack left home again, still with no money yet still possessing his donkey. As he wandered the lanes of the Wolds, he came upon a carpenter's shop. As he was admiring the craftsman's handiwork, the carpenter came out and said, 'Ah, you look a likely lad. I'm looking for a strong youth to help me for a year and a day. I'll give you good wages at the end of that time.'

And so Jack started work. He lived in the house and was given his food, bed and clothes. He worked very hard and very well. When the year and a day was over, the carpenter said, 'This has not been a good time for trading, and so instead of money for your wages, I shall give you a magic table. I have no son or daughter and you have been a good worker. This lovely table will last you the rest of your days. Whenever you need to eat, all you have to do is to rub the surface and say, 'Table be covered' and it will at once become heavy with the finest food and drink. You will never again be hungry.'

Jack thanked him from the bottom of his heart and went on his way with the strong little donkey carrying the table on its back. Eventually he arrived at the Wolds inn where he had lost his other donkey, but even now had no idea that the landlord had exchanged animals. Jack had always thought that his donkey had lost its magic powers, but when the landlord saw him he thought the lad had returned to claim his rightful property. He had no wish to show Jack into the finest parts of the inn, which was now a large hotel with splendid furnishings, but instead showed him into the kitchen of one of his servant's cottages.

'I would like the finest food and wine,' said Jack, knowing that the table would produce whatever the landlord could not.

'I am but a poor landlord,' lied his host. 'I can only offer an egg fried with a slice of bread.'

'Then join me in a feast,' said Jack, still unaware that the man was a thief. 'Allow me to spend the night here with a fine stable for my donkey, and I will provide us both with a feast fit for a king.'

The landlord suspected some kind of trick from this man, but could not refuse and so Jack went outside, lowered the table to the ground and said, 'Table be covered.' Immediately it was covered with the finest of food and wine, and so the two men sat down and ate the feast of a lifetime. Jack, tired but happy, went up to bed and slept soundly.

But as he slept, the crafty landlord went into one of his outbuildings and found a table which looked exactly like Jack's and stood it in its place next to the donkey. He hid Jack's table until the lad had departed. Next morning, Jack thanked the landlord for his hospitality and left, once again heading for his father's house to announce that he was wealthy and that he would now marry Jill.

'Show me your wealth!' demanded his father.

But when Jack pronounced the magic words over the table, nothing happened. He tried and tried but to no avail, and so his father found a broom-handle and began to belabour the lad with it, calling him a liar, a cheat and a ne'er-do-well. Jack ran away from home once more.

As he roamed the Wolds looking for more work, he realized that he had been tricked not once, but twice, by the landlord and set out to find the inn to remonstrate with him. On the way, he came to a deep stream and saw a tall, thin man standing beside it. They fell into conversation and the man said, 'I need to get across this stream, but there is no bridge or boat, nor can I swim a stroke.'

'Never fear,' said Jack. 'I have walked its banks just now

and can make a bridge for you. Follow me.'

He retraced his steps a short distance to a tree whose roots had been partly washed away by the heavy water; Jack climbed it and began to rock backwards and forwards. Soon the tree was swaying tremendously and the remaining roots gave way with a loud crack as the tree fell across the stream to make a fine bridge. Jack returned to the bank and smiled at the man. 'There you are, sir, a bridge!'

'I must thank you, my lad,' said the man. He then produced a magic knife and cut a slender stick from one of the branches of the tree, handing it to Jack. 'This is a magic stick,' said the man who was, in fact, a wizard. 'Take it and whenever you say, "Up stick and at 'em", it will beat anyone who has wronged you in any way. To halt it, you just say, "Down stick".'

Jack was delighted with this and after helping the wizard across the makeshift bridge, went on his way. He found the inn on the Wolds; it was a summer day and all the doors stood open and so he went inside and surprised the landlord. There he was, seated at Jack's table which was laden with the finest of foods, with a pile of gold and silver coins at his elbow.

'Ah, good-day,' began the landlord, but before he could say anything else Jack shouted, 'Up stick and at 'em'. The stick began to wallop the landlord mercilessly, beating him about the head, the arms, the legs and the whole of his body until he was sobbing for mercy. He confessed to the theft of Jack's donkey and the table, and said he would return them if only Jack would call off the stick. 'Down stick,' said Jack and the stick obeyed.

Jack now knew that he could return to his father, announce that he was wealthy, and demand to marry Jill. But his father steadfastly refused to believe that Jack was a rich man and so Jack invited him outside to see a remarkable demonstration. His father stood astonished as the donkey spewed coins from its mouth and as the table covered itself with food and drink.

'Now, I shall marry Jill,' smiled Jack.

'Not if I can stop you!' snarled his father, who was already plotting to steal the table and the donkey from his son.

'Then you must also be taught a lesson!' said Jack who lifted his magic stick and said, 'Up stick and at 'em'. The stick began to beat the unkind, uncaring father until he begged for mercy.

'Call it off,' he shouted.

'Only if you agree to my marriage to Jill,' responded Jack.

And so his father finally consented. Jill had waited as she had promised and so the couple were married and lived happily ever after.

Although the donkey died, it is said that the magic table is still in a farmhouse somewhere on the Wolds, with the precious stick hidden in a secret compartment in one of its drawers.

22   York
The Book of Fate

One of York's most intriguing folk stories begins in a small shop which belonged to a poor shoemaker called Eldric. The dark and dingy premises, often lit even in daytime by candle-light due to their lowly position beneath the overhanging eaves of Stonegate, had been in the cobbler's family for many generations. His father and his grandfather before him had been shoemakers of renown and had worked in this shop which was literally within the shadows of York Minster. They had served all the important people of York, including a succession of Lord Mayors and Archbishops, but in spite of his fame and skill, Eldric was now finding it increasingly difficult to earn enough money to support his family.

The chief problem was his number of children. He had five, all boys, and they constantly needed clothes and food. And how could he find work for them all in this cramped shop when they were old enough? Although he worked very hard for his many customers, the money never seemed to be enough. He could never afford new premises because he could barely find enough money to feed and clothe his family. And then he had materials to buy plus all the costs of running his business.

But worse was to come because his hard-working wife produced yet another child, this time a baby girl. Poor Eldric broke down in despair. He could never cope with another mouth to feed. For him, it seemed the end. There was no hope, nothing he could do; he and his poor family would have to resort to begging to survive.

One sad day as he worked in his shop with the door

open to gain a little extra light, his troubles finally overwhelmed him. He was extremely tired, his body ached with constant work, his normally agile fingers were stiff and weary and there seemed no solution to his problems. The strong Eldric broke down and burst into tears.

By chance, a famous knight was passing along Stonegate at this moment and heard the sobbing deep within the dark little shop. He was Sir Hugh Fitz-Maldred and he halted his beautiful white charger outside as he decided to seek the cause of the noise. He found the unhappy shoemaker slumped over his bench with his head in his hands as he sobbed in unremitting misery.

'Sir,' said the knight. 'Pray tell me. What is the cause of all this?'

Eldric recovered sufficiently to explain that his wife had just given birth to a daughter and that he could not afford to keep her.

'I just do not know what to do,' he told Sir Hugh.

'I will read the child's fortune,' offered the knight. 'My family possesses the famous Book of Fate which will tell all.'

As the knight went out to bring the volume from his saddle-bag, Eldric prepared a glass of ale for his visitor and managed to gain control of his emotions. Sir Hugh soon returned with a large blue book and after briefly quizzing Eldric about the baby girl began to study its pages. Then a look of horror came over his handsome face.

'Sir?' begged Eldric. 'Pray, what is wrong?'

The knight gathered his composure and said, 'I cannot tell thee. But I will solve thy problem immediately – give me the girl child and I shall rear her as if she were mine. She shall have all the riches I can afford and she shall lead the life of a fine lady.'

Eldric did not wish to part with his baby girl for he loved her dearly, but after discussing her dismal future with his wife, they agreed to give her to Sir Hugh. Without that extra tiny person to feed and clothe, Eldric could just pay his way. Sir Hugh promised he would keep the family informed of her progress through life. But as the knight rode away with the baby, he had no such intention. He wanted to get rid of the child. The Book of Fate had revealed that this child of a poor shoemaker would marry his own dear son, Robert, to become mistress of the Fitz-Maldred estates. And he, a knight of the realm, had no wish that his historic family should marry into such a lowly state; that was far beneath their dignity.

Thus he had decided to destroy the baby girl.

He rode rapidly towards the banks of the River Ouse and at a point to the south of the city, not far from where Clifford's Tower now stands, he cast the child into the deep, fast-flowing water, then galloped away as rapidly as he was able.

But the thick warm clothes of the tiny bundle did not sink and the baby stayed afloat; the fast current carried her downstream. Before long, she was swept into some reeds at a bend in the river and there she began to cry. Her voice was heard by a boatman who lived and worked beside the Ouse and when he investigated, he discovered the hungry child. She was lying among the reeds in her wet clothes and apart from being cold and hungry, was quite fit and well.

The boatman's wife had never been able to bear a child and they regarded this baby as a sign from heaven. They took the child home to rear her as their own. The boatman was not rich, for he earned his living by carrying people and goods on his old wooden boat and sometimes supplemented his income by catching and selling freshwater fish. His home was a poor wooden shack beside the river but he was a happy and contented man with a caring and loving wife.

Sixteen years later, Sir Hugh Fitz-Maldred was riding with some friends and their route took them along the banks of the Ouse. They decided to purchase some fish and as they approached the old wooden cottage on the banks of the river, they saw a beautiful maiden standing at the door, her lovely features radiating charm and happiness.

As they galloped on, they all discussed the gracious girl who had dealt with them and wondered which simple countryman would be fortunate enough to marry such a delightful maid. Then, when he had a moment to himself,

Sir Hugh consulted the Book of Fate which he still carried in his saddle-bag. He was horrified to find that she would become the wife of his son, who was still unmarried. And then he realized that this was indeed the baby girl he had tried to drown all those years ago. It was the shoemaker's daughter! He could not allow the marriage under any circumstances and so he devised another scheme to get rid of the girl.

The cunning plan was this. He had a brother who lived at Carnaby near a seaside town now called Bridlington, and Sir Hugh decided to pretend that he had to send him an urgent message about a family matter. But how could the message be delivered when enemies of the Fitz-Maldred family lurked along the route? The answer was an anonymous messenger, a most unlikely person, so who better than a young, unknown girl?

Sir Hugh then went discuss this with the boatman. At first, he resolutely refused to allow his daughter to undertake such a long and perilous journey, but when Sir Hugh exercised all his charm and powers of persuasion, coupled with the promise of a fine reward for the girl upon completion of her task, the boatman agreed. The girl, whose name was Lucia, was excited by this offer for it would enable her to see something of the world beyond the banks of the River Ouse.

Before setting out, she was given a purse of money for her expenses, along with the name of an inn near Fridaythorpe where she could spend the night during her expedition. She was supplied with a reliable horse too and a fine riding-outfit, plus a list of the villages upon the Wolds through which she would pass on her long journey – Murton, Stamford Bridge, Kirby Underdale, Fridaythorpe, Wetwang, Garton-on-the-Wolds, Great Driffield, Ruston Parva, Harpham, Burton Agnes, Haisthorpe and finally Carnaby. It would be a two-day ride at least. And in her purse was the very important letter which had to be delivered personally to Sir Ranulph Fitz-Maldred at his manor in Carnaby. She had no idea what that letter contained.

She enjoyed the first day's riding and reached the inn near Fridaythorpe, tired and hungry, but very contented and happy. After a welcome meal, she collapsed into a warm and comfortable bed and slept soundly; so soundly, in fact, that she did not hear the travelling-thief who entered her room that night. He was seeking money and saw her purse on the chest of drawers near the bed; as he emptied it he found the note. He opened it, thinking it would lead him to even greater riches but was horrified to read,

> Dearest brother, the carrier of this letter is a great enemy of our family. You must put her to death at the first opportunity. In haste, your loving brother, Hugh.

The thief knew the Fitz-Maldreds but was horrified by this threat and now studied his victim more closely. His dull candle revealed the sleeping girl, a true beauty who lay fast asleep and whose face revealed no sign of enmity or cruelty; how could anyone wish to kill her? Surely no one in that esteemed family would send such a note with this lovely maiden? He decided that someone must have exchanged the note, perhaps out of jealousy. He knew that Sir Hugh's son, Robert, was seeking a bride. Surely this must be the girl he sought? She must be on her way to meet him and some jealous rival wished to prevent the marriage! The thief thought fast – the Fitz-Maldreds had been kind to him in the past, he knew the family well, he knew that Sir Ranulph was godfather to the son of Sir Hugh, so the thief decided he would save her life! He replaced her cash in the purse, for there would be other opportunities to steal tonight, and he replaced the note. He rewrote it so that it read,

> Dearest brother, the carrier of this note has all the virtues necessary to become the wife of my beloved son to whom you are godfather. Please ensure that she meets him and marries him. Your loving brother, Hugh.'

When the beautiful maiden arrived at the manor-house and handed over the note, Sir Ranulph was delighted. His nephew Robert was staying at the house, having arrived unexpectedly, and so he was able to introduce the young couple. They fell in love immediately and could not wait to get married, and so Lucia was invited to remain at Carnaby until the wedding.

A huge wedding ceremony was arranged at Bridlington Priory and now Sir Ranulph sent a message to his brother. Lucia sent one to the boatman who had brought her up and so the various families awaited the wonderful day. But Sir Hugh was horrified – all his scheming had gone wrong. How was it that Robert had managed to be at Carnaby? How had the girl escaped? There were no answers and so he jumped onto his fastest horse and galloped across the Wolds to Carnaby.

When he arrived, Lucia was out; she had ridden into Bridlington for the day with the intention of walking along the beach to enjoy some solitude in the fresh air, and it was there that Sir Hugh found her. He had decided, yet again, to kill the girl and as he bore down upon her with his sword upraised, she held up her hands, thinking he was riding to congratulate her. But her open and happy welcome unsettled him.

'I was going to kill thee, woman,' he growled. 'Thou canst never marry my son, we are Fitz-Maldreds of noble descent and we cannot allow the blood-line to be diluted by a commoner. You must never marry my son; if necessary, I shall kill you before I permit the wedding to proceed!'

'But Robert has given me a ring,' and she produced a golden ring from the pocket of her bodice and held it up. 'It is your family ring, it bears your coat of arms. By this, we are betrothed and he will place his wedding-ring on my finger in the priory …'

'He will do no such thing!' Sir Hugh snatched the ring from her and cast it into the grey waters of the North Sea. It sank without trace as Lucia dissolved into tears.

'Now, you must die,' cried the knight.

'No, sir, no. I will do anything, I will disappear, I will never darken your doorstep again if you allow me to live

... I have done no wrong, sir, nor will I ever do wrong ...'

And so Sir Hugh relented and allowed Lucia to live. She walked along the beach, crying in her misery, and not knowing where to turn. She knew she must abandon her former life and family, and that she must find a way of earning a living. She slept overnight in an old barn and was wandering the lanes near the town when she encountered a servant-woman. The woman asked her business and Lucia said she was seeking work. The woman said that her master, Lord de Bessingby, had just lost a good cook and that he was seeking a woman who could manage his kitchens. There was to be a huge 21st-birthday party for Lord de Bessingby's daughter at the manor in three months time and so he needed someone very dependable.

Lucia got the job. She started work in the kitchens of Bessingby Manor just outside Bridlington and soon established herself as a fine cook. The lessons taught her by the boatman's wife now stood her in good stead and very soon her meals were the talk of the district. She would have no difficulty coping with the birthday party.

As she worked on the huge meal, she could watch the arrival of the guests, and was startled to see Sir Hugh, Sir Ranulph and their ladies and Robert Fitz-Maldred dismounting outside. They were in their finest clothes; they were guests!

She thanked God that she would never come face to face with them, for her work would keep her downstairs and so she busied herself with the meal. And then, as she cut open a huge fish, she was startled to see a gold ring glittering within. It was hers – the one that Sir Hugh had cast into the waves all those weeks ago – the betrothal ring of the Fitz-Maldreds! She rinsed it and slid it on to her finger then continued with her work.

She marvelled at the coincidence. The ring had reappeared at the very place her lover had also reappeared. It was almost as if fate was guiding her life. But she knew she could not reveal herself. Besides, Robert would not recognize her; her hair was in a different style, she was wearing a white cap, her clothing was that of a cook, not a lady, and she knew that her face was fatter now, due to all the good food that was so available. But, unknown to Lucia, it was the custom at Bessingby Manor that after a celebratory meal, the cooks, waiters, wine-waiters, servants and all those who had helped prepare the banquet were introduced to the guests. But when Lord de Bessingby made the introductions in the splendid banqueting-hall, he made a special mention of the young cook who had arrived so recently and with such success.

She had made such a fine job of all the family meals, and especially this banquet he said, and he bade her step forward to receive their approbation. But when Lucia obeyed, she was recognized by Sir Hugh, in spite of her changed appearance. In a sudden rage he drew his sword. He was about to slay her before the assembled guests when she held up her hand to ward off his blow, and he saw the gold ring.

He seized her arm and glared at it.

'Sir,' she whimpered. 'It was in the fish that you ate at dinner ... ' and she explained the recovery of the ring.

Sir Hugh sank to his knees before her, now fully appreciating that the Book of Fate had been correct. What must be, must be! No one could, or should, attempt to interfere with someone's fate. After all her trials, he could understand that this girl was destined to be the bride of his son, the future mistress of the Fitz-Maldred estates, and there was no way that that course of events could, or should, be altered. Full of remorse for his behaviour and in atonement for his murderous intentions, Sir Hugh rode to Bridlington Priory to spend three days in deep penance. Before leaving, he announced that Robert and Lucia would have the finest of weddings. And Eldric, the poor shoemaker of York, his wife and all their sons would be invited, as would the boatman and his wife.

Lady Lucia and Sir Robert Fitz-Maldred, as he became upon the death of his father, lived happily ever after.

23   York
Brother Jucundus

One of the jolliest of Yorkshire folk stories is the tale of
Brother Jucundus. Jucundus was not his real name, but
the one he had chosen upon entering the monastery. It
was a Latin word, the language of his Church, and was
taken from Psalm CXI. It meant 'Acceptable'.

Jucundus was a most unlikely monk; round, fat, jolly
and middle-aged, he loved food and wine, and thoroughly
enjoyed being with happy people. He especially enjoyed
parties and outings accompanied by music, singing and
dancing.

It was something of a mystery, therefore, as to why he
became a brother within St Leonard's priory in York.
There, his life was a long round of prayers and fasting,
beginning at daybreak and continuing late into the night.
Jucundus adopted this style of life with the full intention
of becoming an ordained monk after his period of
instruction. There is little doubt, however, that in those
long hours, Jucundus often reminisced about massive
feasts accompanied by bottles of the best wine and all
enjoyed to the singing and dancing of pretty girls. He had
enjoyed all such things before entering the priory.

But now he was surrounded by the trappings of his
calling and subjected to the strict rules of the monastery;
even the adjoining premises was another religious
establishment. It was St Mary's Abbey, separated from St
Leonard's only by a thick, high wall. The only other music
he heard was the singing of those unseen monks who
were his near neighbours.

There were times when he wished he could go into the

city of York to enjoy himself, just for one night, but his superiors were always aware of the temptations of the flesh and they kept a close eye on the jolly student monk. They knew he was restless and wondered whether indeed he was suitable to be ordained a priest. But in those testing moments, Brother Jucundus was trapped.

All he could do was sigh with frustration and wish he was able to free himself of the restraints of his religious vocation. But he had become a brother and for at least another year must honour the promises he had made when accepting this calling; after that time, he could then decide whether or not to accept ordination as a full monk in holy orders. But as a brother, he must abide by the monastery's strict rules and regulations.

One of those rules was that each afternoon, after a modest lunch, the brothers had to return to their cells for a period of private prayer. In his quiet cell one day, however, Jucundus could not concentrate because there were very happy noises outside. He could hear chatter and laughter, music and singing, all accompanied by the unmistakeable sounds of a busy fair in progress. There were side-shows, games and sports, food and drink – he could hear it all! It was Bootham Fair, and it was so close to his cell, so close …

The temptation was too much for the merry brother. He decided that he must, on this solitary occasion, escape from the confines of the priory and join the fun of the fair. He opened the door of his cell and listened – all his fellow brethren were in their own cells, deep in prayer; he could hear them muttering and saying their rosaries and so he tiptoed along the corridor to the porter's lodge. There was no one about – everyone was at prayer, even the prior. He managed to find some money in an alms-box and helped himself to some coins. Then, sneaking the big key from the board in the porter's lodge, he unlocked the gate of the priory and let himself out. Still in his monastic robes, he hurried into Bootham where he joined the crowds and began to enjoy all the fun of the fair.

The people loved him. They gave him wine and ale, food and sweets, they took him to the side-shows and let him take part in the games. They they gave him more wine

and ale, took him on the swings and roundabouts and
very soon, Brother Jucundus forgot that he was a holy
man. He drank until he was very merry indeed and found
himself on a seesaw, being raised into the air by the
weight of two young men at the other end. He sang:

> In dulce jubilo
> Up, up and up we go ...

But as he was lifted high into the air, he noticed two
monks from his priory; when his absence had been
noticed, they had been sent to find him and now stood
and watched as he sang his little song at the end of the
seesaw. Down he came, singing:

> In dulce jubilo,
> Down, down down we go ...

Because of his tipsy condition, the monks had to
half-carry him back to the priory. He kept singing 'In dulce
jubilo' and because of his lack of repentance, they took
him to the prior. The prior listened to the story of his
disgraceful behaviour and decided that Jucundus must
pay the penalty – death by being sealed alive in a thick
wall.

Four monks carried him down the stone steps into the
bowels of the priory, but he was still drunk and still
singing. They took him to a tiny room which led off the
wine-cellar, seated him on a wooden stool and gave him a
crust of bread and a jug of water. Then more brethren
arrived with stones and mortar and began the awful work
of sealing their brother in what was to become his tomb.
He cheerfully watched them at work, not comprehending
what they were really doing, and continued to sing his
merry songs. Before long, he fell asleep as the work
continued around him.

Finally, there was a small gap left at which the prior
came to pray for the soul of Brother Jucundus. Having
done this, the final gap was sealed and Brother Jucundus
was left to his awful, lingering death. He slept for many
hours in the pitch darkness of his stone coffin-to-be; it was

roughly where the Theatre Royal now stands and in fact, even today, there is a cellar beneath the theatre. Could this be where Jucundus was incarcerated?

In time, the effects of the liquor wore off and he awoke. He was cold and hungry, and had no idea where he was. As Jucundus began to explore the tiny place with his hands, all he could feel was the cold stone which encased him. There was no door, no window and no way out. He began to realize what had happened – he had been walled in while still alive. He began to shout, but no one came and as the air became in short supply, Jucundus started to kick and press against the walls. As he pressed his strong back against one wall, it gave a little; now encouraged, he placed his feet against one wall and his back against the other, levering himself into a position from where he could exert the most pressure. And the wall behind him collapsed.

Jucundus found himself thrown among a tumble of stones and mortar. He blinked in the bright light and rubbed his arms and legs, bruised by the falling stones, but that didn't matter; at least he was alive.

He was in a cellar, but it was not the cellar of St Leonard's priory! It was a strange place and so, very gingerly, he made his way up the steps and along the corridor above. There was no one about, everything was quiet and very soon, from the furnishings and adornments, he realized where he was. He was in another monastery! With some trepidation, Jucundus realized he was in the confines of St Mary's abbey.

His heart sank. This was an enclosed order and the monks spent their time in silence! They ate only the most meagre of meals with no wine and their routine was even harsher than that of St Leonard's. But he had no choice but to join them if he was to survive and so he walked through the corridors and joined the many black-robed monks who walked around in silence. No one asked him who he was.

In his own robes, they thought he was a novice who had just joined them and the guest master showed him to a cell. The bed was harder than his previous one, but he thanked God that he was still alive and decided that he had no alternative but to join the routine of the monks of St Mary's. Thus he began another round of prayers, meditation and manual work, but the poor food and tough life style soon caused his weight to reduce. Within a year, Jucundus was a slender, fit and healthy man, if rather unhappy.

But his work there had drawn him to the attention of the abbot and on the only day in the year when the monks could speak, Easter Sunday, the abbot asked Jucundus if he would accept a special responsibility. Jucundus said he would be pleased – it might lead to an end of the monotony. The abbot then said he wanted Jucundus to be the cellarer.

Jucundus was delighted. This meant he was in charge of the wine which was issued on feast-days and other special occasions, or when the abbey received guests, and it also meant he could find a reason for going into the cellars whenever he wanted – he could say he was checking stocks or preparing wines for some particular event.

Then, on 7 May, the feast-day of St John of Beverley who was a local saint, the monks had a celebratory Mass followed by a special meal. It was the duty of Jucundus to supply the wine and he had gone to the cellar some time before the meal to prepare it. He had tasted some from a special cask, and then some more and yet still more as he tried to decide which to issue to the brethren for this feast. As he tested more and more of the very best wine, he forgot about the monks who by now had assembled in the refectory and were awaiting their drink. The abbot was there too, and some important guests.

As they began to grow impatient, the abbot decided to seek the cellarer and, not speaking a word, marched off to locate Jucundus.

All the other monks followed, angry but unable to speak their concern and they were horrified when the abbot discovered Jucundus. There he was, lying on the floor among dozens of empty bottles and opened casks, singing to himself and waving a tankard around as these words reached the ears of the brethren:

> In dulce jubilo
> Up, up and up we go ...

Such was the gravity of the sin of gluttony in their view, that they broke their vows of silence as they decided what punishment to impose upon this erring fellow. Their decision was unanimous – Jucundus would be excommunicated and then walled into the cellar, the scene of his awful crime. He would be left to a lingering death. With no more ado, they mixed some mortar, gave him a newly-baked loaf of bread and a beaker of water, and then pushed him into a space deep in the cellar. With some loose stones lying conveniently nearby, they walled him in as he sat on the floor, singing:

> In dulce jubilo
> Up, up and up we go ...

They said a prayer for the repose of his soul and fitted the final stone; thus Jucundus was once again walled into a dark tomb and, at this stage, he had no idea where he was. He sang to himself as he sat on the floor, for he had a fine voice.

It transpired that the adjoining priory of St Leonard was also celebrating St John's feast-day and their cellarer had gone into the cellars to select the wines. As he studied the range of bottles, he heard faint singing coming from behind the wall. He was amazed! It sounded like Brother Jucundus, but he had been incarcerated there more than a year ago!

He stopped his work and pressed his ear to the wall. It *was* Jucundus – he'd know that voice anywhere! He was still alive, after all this time! It was a miracle ...

To be sure he was not imagining the voice, the cellarer sent for the other monks; there was no prior now, for he had died and the priory was in the process of electing someone to take his place. And so they all came to listen and were astonished. There were emotions of mixed happiness and fear as the monks hurriedly sought tools to break down the wall.

And when they removed the stones, there they found Jucundus, slimmer than when they had last seen him, but very much alive and singing:

In dulce jubilo
Up, up and up we go ...

The bread they had given him was still there – and still warm, and he had not drunk his water either! It was indeed a miracle and they then realized they had treated him far too harshly.

'Brother Jucundus – he shall be our new prior. It is a sign from heaven, it is verily a miracle.'

And so Jucundus was carried shoulder-high up the steps and into the fine church where he was immediately ordained and installed as prior of St Leonard's. He remained prior until his death many years later, and in that time he made everyone happy and cheerful. Under his jovial command, St Leonard's priory became a place of happiness and great joy. It was all very acceptable.

24 York
The Minster Fires

When York Minster burst into flames on 9 July 1984, a new folk story was born. Some said the fire was a display of the wrath of God who had objected to the consecration of the controversial Bishop of Durham in the minster less than a week earlier, and it is fairly certain that this belief will now enter the annals of York's folk history.

But this was not the only disastrous fire at York Minster and accounts of two earlier ones can now be included.

It is impossible to outline the history of York Minster in this small volume, save to say that the first church on this site was a small wooden structure dating from the seventh century (see Goodmanham). It is now the largest Gothic church in Europe and one of the most beautiful of English buildings. Its official name is the Metropolitan Church of St Peter, and it is both a cathedral and a minster. A cathedral is a church with a bishop's throne while the name 'minster' implies that it was once a centre of Christian teaching or ministering. The name minster has not been given to any church since the Reformation, when it was possible for a church to be a minster while not enjoying the status of cathedral. There are four minsters in Yorkshire – York, Beverley, Stonegrave and Kirkdale. Of these, only York ranks as a cathedral, but all now serve as Anglican churches.

With a history as ancient as that of York Minster, it would be strange if it was not the source of some folk-tales and indeed some are included elsewhere in this volume (see the Horn of Ulphus, the Miracles of St William and the chapter on Goodmanham). One continuing piece of lore concerns the everpresent scaffolding of the minster – there is a persistent belief that if ever York Minster is free from scaffolding, it will be restored to the Catholic faith from which it was removed as a result of the Reformation. It is likely that the present scaffolding will remain until the year 2000.

But it is the story of three major fires which have become part of York's folklore, and two of them feature the Bishop of Durham.

One occurred in February 1829 when a religious maniac called Jonathan Martin deliberately set fire to York Minster. Martin was born at Hexham in Northumberland in 1782, the son of poor but honest parents. He became an apprentice tanner and when he was 21, decided to move to London. There he met a man who asked if he was seeking work and who then offered Martin a job on a frigate heading for India. But he found himself involved with a press-gang and was soon on board a ship called *Hercules*, which was part of Lord Nelson's 1804 expedition against Copenhagen.

He spent a lot of time at sea and at one stage was asked by an African to murder some English people in order to steal their valuables. Martin refused and tried to convert the would-be assassin to Christianity.

It was a trip to the Holy Land which turned him further towards religion; there he took a particular delight in visiting biblical locations and his shipmates nicknamed him Parson Saxe. They said he was inclined to argue about religion even if he did not pray very much and that he was very prone to long sulks and outbursts of tears. According to Martin's own life story, he enjoyed some amazing adventures at sea but his colleagues said he imagined most of his daring deeds. One of his tales involved a sailor who was in charge of the gunpowder-room – the fellow shot himself through the head and set fire to the furnishings, whereupon Martin and four colleagues rushed in and managed to extinguish the fire before it blew up the ship and killed all 600 men.

Martin was often punished for drunkenness, and fell overboard on several occasions. He was disliked by most of the men, especially the officers, one reason being that he would cry when punished and then pray while cursing those who had hurt him. He was open in his hatred of Catholics too, then suddenly claimed God had advised him to leave the seafaring life.

He went to live at Norton-on-Tees where he married and had a son called Richard. He worked on a farm and attended the Methodist Chapel at Yarm on Sunday evenings, and the parish church at Norton on Sunday mornings where he took communion. But in time, he turned against the Church of England and became a committed Methodist. On one occasion, he hid in a church pulpit and suddenly stood up to preach from Mark 4: 21–3, accompanied by wild gesticulations. He was removed by churchwardens.

He began to write letters to clergymen and church-members, exorting them to beware of Popery, and very rapidly he became an embarrassment to the Methodists of Yarm. As a result, he was expelled. He set about a preaching tour of the north, visiting Whitby, Bishop Auckland and other places before returning to Norton; then he decided that his wife had turned against him. He went to Newcastle to visit his brother and obtained an old pistol; upon his return to Norton, his wife asked why he wanted a pistol and he said he was going to shoot the Bishop of Durham, but she managed to hide it. News of his alleged intention to murder the Bishop resulted in his appearance before the magistrates and he was sent to a lunatic asylum, first at West Auckland and then at Gateshead.

Whilst inside, he was told that his wife was dying of cancer and he asked to be allowed home to see her and his son, now aged seven, but, according to Martin, such requests were not allowed.

He escaped on 17 June 1820, but was caught at Norton and returned to Gateshead; but on 1 July the same year, while wearing leg-irons, he broke through the ceiling of his cell, got into the garret and escaped through the tiles of the roof. He was now free after three years of captivity and was to remain free until after his crime of arson at York Minster.

His leg-irons were removed by a sympathetic relation of

his mother's, a Mr Kell, and Martin then moved from relation to relation as the police and the asylum authorities searched for him. He went to Glasgow and Edinburgh, but came back to Norton where his wife was desperately ill. He managed to visit her in the final stages of her life, then decided to visit a brother who was a noted artist in London, travelling from Darlington on 1 August 1820 with money given by another friend. But he got no further than Boroughbridge when he was informed that his wife had died, his house had been burgled and £24 cash stolen.

He went to Hull and obtained work in a tannery; when he began to preach to his workmates, they poured a bucket of bull's blood over his head and tormented him so much that he left. He returned to Norton and was there examined by the authorities who said he was fit enough not to return to the lunatic asylum. He got a job as a tanner in Darlington and remained there until 1827, albeit preaching in his spare time.

He then moved to Lincoln where the cathedral impressed him and there wrote his biography – although he could not even spell or compose a correct sentence, he sold the first two editions and had a further 5,000 copies printed! Then in 1828, he met a woman called Maria Hodgson, twenty years his junior, and they were married in Boston. From there, they came to live in York, travelling on Boxing Day 1828, and secured lodgings with a shoemaker called William Lawn. Lawn lived at no. 60, Aldwark, York.

Jonathan Martin soon became a familiar figure in and around the city, selling his books while wearing a glazed, broad-brimmed, low-crowned hat and a black leather cape which came down to his elbows. It had a square patch of fur sewn on the back and this extended from one corner to the other. He attended Methodist meetings in York, alternating between groups known as Primitives and those called Ranters, and spent his spare time reading the Bible or a hymn-book.

Then in January 1829, this notice appeared on one of York Minster's iron gates. It was fastened with a shoemaker's wax thread and this is what it said (sic):

York, Janrey the 5-1829

'Hear the word of Lord, Oh you Dark and Lost Clergymen. Repent and cry For Marcey for know is the day of vangens and your Cumplet Destruction is at Hand for the Lord will not sufer you and the deveal and your blind Hellish Docktren to dseve the works of His Hands no longer.

Oh, you desevears will not milleons of the mighty and rich men of the Earth have to curs the Day that ever they gat under your blind Docktren know to be shamd of your selvs and wepe for your bottls of wine and your downey beds will be taken away from you I warn you to repent in the name of Jesuse and believe he is able on Earth to forgeve sines, for there is no repenting in the greave Oh you blind gydes are yhou not like the man that bilt his house upon the Sandes when the thunder Starmes of Gods Heavey vangens lites upon your gildrys heads a way gos your sandey foundaytons and you to the deepest pet of Hell re Serve the Curses of millions that your blind Docktens has decevd and to reseve Gods heve curs and the Ward pronounst Depart you Carsit blind gides in the Hotist plase of Hell to be tormented with the deveal and all his Eanguls for ever and ever.

Jona. Martin, a frind of the Sun of Boneypart Must conclude by warning you again. Oh, repent, He will soon be able to act

The part of his father

Derect for Jonathan Martin,
Adwark no. 60.

The letter was taken to the canons of York Minster who thought it too absurd to heed, but another was found within the minster on Wednesday 21 January, and further manuscripts followed. In some of them, Martin said, 'Your great churches and minsters will fall down on your guilty heads,' but no one really thought this man was a genuine threat to the minster and no precautions were taken to protect the building.

On 27 January Martin said he and his wife were going to live in Leeds and they arrived on 28, lodging in Brick

Street. He attended the Methodist Chapel and seems to have been happy and normal. He left home on Saturday morning, between 9 a.m. and 10 a.m., and said he had an appointment near Tadcaster. He told his wife he would return to Leeds on the following Monday in time for dinner.

But in fact, he went to York and asked William Lawn if he could use his old room at the lodgings in Aldwark. This was allowed; that Saturday afternoon, he was seen walking around the minster yard and showing great interest in the western towers. He returned to his lodgings and stayed there overnight on the Saturday, leaving at eleven o'clock on Sunday morning.

He went to York Minster and attended morning service, then left. He returned in the afternoon and entered the south transept, walking around the church until the next service began. He was seen by the sexton, Job Knowles, who was ringing the bell for prayers. By this stage, Martin was equipped with a razor with a white shaft which he was to use instead of a steel, a flint, tinder, matches and a penny-candle cut in two. Later, this quickly burnt away, so he stole one of the minster's own candles.

During the service, he hid himself behind Archbishop Grinfield's tomb and remained there until everyone had left. Then he emerged to look for the best site for his fire. The ringers were still in the belfry but they now came out and he watched them leave; they did not lock the door behind them. Martin went into the belfry and struck a light. A man who was passing the minster at 8.30 saw the light, but thought it was the ringers and ignored it. Two prisoners in Peter Prison saw a light in the belfry around nine o'clock but had no reason to think it was anything suspicious.

He left the belfry and by using a ladder he made from the prayer-bell's rope, managed to gain entry to the choir where he struck another light. With the razor, he cut three yards of gold fringe, two gold tassels and some other pieces from the pulpit, crimson velvet curtains from the dean's seat and the precentor's seat at the end of the choir, and some more from the archbishop's throne. He then obtained some cushions and prayer-books, tearing the leaves out of the latter to use for igniting the fabrics, and arranged these items in two heaps near some carved woodwork. He set fire to them, then set about finding a way out of the minster, clutching a Bible he had stolen.

He found a machine used for cleaning the minster and dragged it towards a window in the west aisle of the north transept, climbed onto it and broke the window with a pair of shoemaker's pincers he had brought from his lodgings.

Tying one end of his rope-ladder to the machine, he climbed out of the window and lowered himself to the ground. He left the pincers behind. It was just after 3 a.m. on the morning of 2 February. Candlemas Day.

By this time, the minster's security officer had finished his patrol. He had gone home at 2.30 a.m. without noticing anything untoward. At 4 a.m., a passer-by noticed a light inside the minster but thought it was workmen and did not investigate. At 5 a.m., some explosions were heard, but no one considered investigating the cause.

At 7 a.m., a chorister called Swinbank was on his way to the minster to rehearse before morning service; this was his usual practice, but when he arrived the doors were locked. While waiting for someone to open them, he amused himself by sliding up and down on some ice in the minster yard but fell flat on his back. From that position, he saw smoke coming from the roof of the minster.

The lad went immediately to raise the alarm, calling on the sexton, Job Knowles, to collect the keys, but when he returned, some builders, reporting for work on the minster, had already opened the door. They were met by a pall of thick smoke; it was so dense that entry was impossible. One of them, however, managed to get into the vestry where a small fire engine was kept. He brought it into an aisle to play water on the place where the communion-plate was kept, but already much of the previous carved woodwork of the minster had been destroyed.

Inside, there was a wealth of treasures to be saved and there is no doubt that those men, first on the scene, did some valuable work before the arrival of the Yorkshire Insurance fire-engine. The alarm was spread throughout York by ringing the bells of the nearby church of St Michael-le-Belfry. An army fire-engine arrived, complete with a contingent from the 7th Dragoon Guards and another engine from the city arrived. By ten minutes to eight, the roof was on fire, lead was melting and pieces of burning timber were beginning to fall and cause further fires.

By eight o'clock, the organ had been consumed and soon the minster was a scene of utter horror. The fire-engines present were making little impact and a request went out to bring some from Leeds. At ten to nine, the roof fell in; more private fire-engines owned by country gentlemen began to arrive and there was great concern that the entire east end of the minster should collapse, and with it the famous Great East stained glass window. The size of a tennis-court, it contains the largest area of stained glass in England and is one of the most important windows in the whole world. Fortunately, it survived. By noon, the fire was under control but immense damage had been caused, and at 2 p.m., the Norwich Union's fire-engine arrived from Leeds, closely followed by three further engines. They were able to contain the blaze and as one spectator said, 'What a splendid subject for Martin!' She was referring to the famous artist of that name, little knowing that his brother was responsible for the blaze.

Afterwards, an inquiry soon ascertained that the fire was the work of an incendiary, as an arsonist was then termed, and discovery of the shoemaker's pincers near the escape window soon pointed towards the strange Jonathan Martin.

After leaving the minster at 3 a.m., Martin had made his way to Easingwold where he had a pint of ale, then Thirsk, where he arrived at 11 a.m. He went on to Northallerton, arriving by 3 p.m., and then made his way to West Auckland in County Durham.

He was heading for the home of his old friend, Mr Kell, but it wasn't long before the newspapers carried a report of the blaze and a drawing of the suspect, named as

Jonathan Martin. When he was arrested, he was still in possession of items he had stolen from the minster, including twenty-two feet of crimson velvet and a small Bible. Martin readily admitted his crime; he seemed to believe he had a mission to burn down the minster, possibly because it had been built by Catholics, and he was arraigned at York Assizes on Monday 30 March 1829, charged with arson and sacrilege. He pleaded not guilty to both charges and in fact the verdict in each case was 'Not guilty on the grounds of insanity'.

Jonathan Martin was ordered to be detained during His Majesty's pleasure and was sent to a mental institution, St Luke's Hospital, in London. He remained there until his death.

The cost of his fire was enormous, well over £100,000 at that time, and the entire choir was destroyed, along with some fifteenth-century canopy stalls and many other treasures.

The second fire occurred only eleven years later, but this was not a deliberate action. On 20 May 1840, a careless workman, sometimes described as a clock repairer, left a candle burning in the south-west tower and this set the tower alight. It caused the bells to crash to the ground with what was described as a deep, hollow sound. The nave suffered severe damage as did its wooden roof, and the tower was gutted.

There have been other fires, some fairly minor. One broke out on 19 September 1069 only eight days after Bishop Ealdred had been buried there; the choir caught fire in 1137, and there was a small fire in 1909 when a blaze in the lower roof of the western aisle caused little damage. In February 1971, some tarpaulin burst into flames in the north-west tower, and in 1972 some woodwork in the choir-stalls was damaged by a small blaze.

But worldwide attention was focused on York Minster in July 1984 when a massive fire broke out in the timber-beamed roof of the south transept. The alarm was raised by fire detectors at 2.30 a.m. but by that time the roof was well ablaze, some flames roaring up to 200 feet in the air. The fire had probably been burning for some twenty minutes by that time. The roof collapsed at

3.30 a.m. and there were fears for the minsters' treasures, especially the famous Round Window.

The North Yorkshire Fire Brigade was on the scene in less than four minutes of the alarm being raised and there is no doubt that their prompt and efficient response prevented a greater disaster. Even so, the entire roof of the south transept was lost, along with many treasures kept within; the windows, although suffering some damage as their glass cracked in the heat, could be repaired but the Rose Window, with over 8000 panes of glass, suffered severely.

Ironically, that window had also suffered in Martin's fire when the heat caused cracks to appear in the glass. After the 1984 fire, the window was meticulously repaired by local craftsmen.

In 1984, there was the inevitable smoke-damage to much of the building combined with loss of treasures, burnt woodwork and massive damage to a whole range of objects in both the transept and other parts of the minster. But, as always, the mighty church was restored, albeit at a cost in the region of £3 million, and it is now in splendid condition.

But what was the cause of this ruinous blaze?

There was an electrical storm at the time. At least eighteen witnesses claimed to have seen lightning strike the minster shortly before the blaze. It was known that a 'weather cell' had formed near York at 1.56 that morning, and experts said that several million volts had struck the minster, overcoming its lightning conductors to ignite the roof-timbers.

But other experts discount this, saying that the electrical storm was some distance from York and that those who saw the lightning could not be sure it had actually struck the minster. The sky was full of lightning flashes at the time. But two girls, then aged eighteen, independently stated that they had seen a bolt of lightning strike the minster sometime between 1.30 and 2 a.m. that morning. One lived in Heworth and the other in Osbaldwick and each saw the strike from her bedroom window. The theory of a lightning strike remains the most likely.

But the story which has already entered the folklore of York is that the fire was divine retribution from God.

After Professor David Jenkins was appointed Bishop of

Durham, he antagonized many Christians of different denominations by openly stating that he doubted the reality of Christ's resurrection and likewise doubted the Virgin Birth. Only days before the York Minster fire, this beautiful church had been used for his consecration as the Bishop of Durham. It was said that the mystery fire was God's way of showing his displeasure.

To this day, there are still arguments about how the fire started.

25 York
The Ghosts of Trinity Church

York is Britain's most haunted city, with sightings ranging from a spectral man in a modern shopping arcade to a legion of Roman soldiers marching through the cellars of the Treasurer's House. This band of tired-looking soldiers is probably the greatest number of ghosts ever seen at one time. Many of the city's ghosts are solitary characters and their haunts are well-documented; tourists who seek these visitors from the past can obtain guide-books which explain where and when to see their favourite ghost. Guided tours of haunted sites have become one of York's main tourist attractions.

This book is not a collection of ghost-stories, however, but in one case, a multiple haunting has been witnessed so very frequently that it has entered the realms of folklore. For that reason, it is included here. The case is of interest because there are contemporary and realistic accounts of the repeated appearance of Trinity's famous three ghosts.

The tale features Holy Trinity Church which is in Micklegate, York. This old cobbled street with its fine Georgian buildings curves from Micklegate Bar as it sweeps downhill towards the city centre. One of the streets leading off Micklegate is Trinity Lane; Holy Trinity Church is situated near that point.

Nearby is a beautiful old half-timbered house called Jacob's Well, and the area boasts other ancient churches, one of which is now an arts centre.

The ghosts of Trinity Church do not seem to have made a recorded appearance before 1866, so we are fortunate to have access to a first-hand account. It was written by a

clergyman whose name is not given. When he wrote to
the Victorian author, historian and folklore expert, the
Reverend Sabine Baring-Gould, he signed the statement
simply 'A.B.'

The Reverend A.B. said he was in the gallery at the west
end of Trinity Church when he saw an apparition on the
bottom half of the stained glass window at the east end.
He described the sighting as having the same effect as that
of a slide being drawn through a magic lantern (an early
version of a slide projector). We might compare it with a
moving film shown against a background of stained glass.

This clergyman witness took into account the fact that
the movements could have been something ordinary and
explicable such as the movements of trees or flags outside,
or even the reflection of people in the church grounds. But
those possibilities were thoroughly examined and
discounted.

The figures are very recognizable as human beings. The
group of three does not always appear together and
sometimes there is a solitary figure. When the solitary one
makes an appearance, it is most often dressed in a white
garment, rather like a clergyman's surplice, and it is said
to be female. If the three make a simultaneous appearance,
they are usually seen on Trinity Sunday.

When A.B. was present, on one of the Sundays after
Trinity, he clearly saw three figures, so he states that he
can vouch for the fact that the three figures do appear on
days other than Trinity Sunday.

According to A.B., he saw three figures, two women
and one a child. The two women were very distinct in
appearance, one being tall and graceful, and the other
medium-sized. The second woman was seen to caress the
child during the absence of the mother and wring her
hands over it, and for this reason she has become known
as the nursemaid. Each figure was very clearly seen by
A.B. and, as he said, 'After they have been seen once or
twice, they are at once recognizable.'

It is evident from that statement that they used to make
regular appearances although they did not follow
precisely the same movements on each occasion. Their
routine, almost like a stage-play, was varied slightly upon

each occasion although there was a fairly general order; the mother would come from the north side of the window and when she reached halfway she would stop, turn around and wave her hand towards the area from which she had come.

At this sign, the nursemaid and the child would appear, and both women would bend over the child as if experiencing some great concern about it. The taller woman, the mother, always seemed to be the more worried of the two and after a while she would move to the far side of the window, i.e. the south side, taking the child with her. The nursemaid remained in the centre of the window and then slowly moved back to the north side from which she had come, all the time waving as if in farewell. After the mother and child had disappeared, the nursemaid would reappear as if seeking them.

She would be seen bending forward in anticipation of greeting the child who always reappeared from the portion of the window from which it and its mother had disappeared. This would be accompanied by more gestures of apparent despair and concern, after which all three would leave together from the north side of the window, the side where they had made their original appearance. It was almost like the repeat of a film, for it seems the ghosts liked to appear when music was being played; on one occasion, they appeared during an eight-line hymn and remained throughout it, all the time making frantic gestures about the child. In one case, it was said that the ghosts 'rushed on (in stage phrase) and remained during a whole hymn' and the louder the music, the more grief they expressed.

In 1866, some eight years after this series of sightings, another witness wrote to Baring-Gould under the initials S.L. He said he had visited the gallery of Trinity Church on many occasions in the hope of catching sight of the ghosts, but had never done so. Then one dull day with rain falling outside he took shelter in the church and chanced to look at the east window; it was then filled with plain green glass and the organ stood in front of it.

He noticed a movement outside the window and saw the figure of a graceful girl of about eighteen or twenty years of age. She crossed in front of the window with a light, free step and was covered entirely with a fine lace veil which clearly showed the outline of her head and figure, although her features were not visible.

The witness described the veil as being pure white, flowing behind her like a train as she walked past the window. She reappeared two or three minutes later, her veil still flowing behind her.

Some have felt that this figure was not one of the three seen earlier, but that it was the ghost of a nun; there had been a monastery on the site of Holy Trinity Church in medieval times.

But in 1876, another witness described his experience in this old church. He signed himself H.G.T.F. and said that he attended a service in the church on Easter Day 1876. He was seated in the gallery but his seat did not enjoy a particularly good view of the east window because there was a chandelier between him and the lower panes. But in the middle of the service, his attention was drawn to a bright light which passed rapidly from north to south across the window in a smooth, gliding motion. It was outside the church and was in the form of a female, robed and hooded.

He noted that there were four divisions to the window, all of stained glass, but at the edge of each there ran a rim of plain transparent glass about two inches wide. This rim adjoined the stonework of the walls and it was through this that H.G.T.F. saw the vision. He had difficulty describing precisely what he had seen, except that it was 'like a form, transparent but yet thick (if such a term can be used) with light.' The robe did not resemble linen, it was far brighter, long and trailed like a bridal-train. Then the ghost passed out of sight behind the wall.

Half an hour later, the ghost reappeared and again moved across the window from north to south; it remained for some ten seconds and returned with what he described as a child, then stopped at the last pane and vanished. He did not see the child again, but after a few seconds, the woman reappeared and crossed the last part of the window very rapidly.

It is reported that Sunday-schoolchildren would sit in

the gallery to watch the three ghosts and the youngsters saw them so frequently that they called them 'the mother, the nurse and the child.'

The repeated sighting of the Trinity ghosts has given rise to stories which seek to explain their presence. One tale accounts for the appearance of the nun-like figure. At the time of the Reformation, Trinity Church was the site of a monastic institution. When Henry VIII decided to ransack and demolish the nation's abbeys, a band of rough soldiers arrived to carry out his orders. They had instructions to close the monastery, destroy its Catholic artefacts and seize its wealth for the king. When the abbess refused to admit them, they smashed down the door but she stood inside the entrance, a brave and determined woman. With immense courage and devotion to the nuns and religious institution in her care, she denied the soldiers entry, saying that if they wished to close the convent and steal its treasures, then they would do so over her dead body. And, she added, if they did slay her, then her restless spirit would return to haunt the premises until they redressed their wrongdoing.

But the leader, known as Sir Ralph, was in no mood to be defeated by a nun, however noble her cause, and he ran his sword through her body. The nuns shrieked in horror at the sight and wept at her savage death, but Henry's commissioners carried out their duty. An old verse tells the story and part of it says:

> The house she loved is levelled,
> The church has seen decay,
> And other worshippers are found,
> Where once she loved to pray.
> But faithful to her promise,
> Thro' all these changing years,
> Within those sacred precincts still,
> The Phantom Nun appears.

But if this tale explains the appearance of the nun-like figure, it does not explain the mother, her child and the nursemaid.

One possible explanation lies in a story which has come

to us from the fifteenth century. It concerns a family, father, mother and only child, (although we are not told whether the child was a girl or a boy) who were devoted to one another. However, the father died prematurely and was buried at the east end of Holy Trinity Church, very close to the east window. Later, as the mother struggled to bring up her child alone, there was a terrible outbreak of the plague in York and the child was affected. Its mother sought the services of a nurse, but her ministrations were unsuccessful.

The child died from the disease and the mother wished it to be buried beside its father. But the authorities would not allow it. It was a rule, during the plague, that any deceased sufferer must be buried in a communal plague-pit outside the city walls and not in any of the city's churchyards because of a fear of spreading the contamination. And so the child had to be buried in an awful mass grave somewhere beyond Micklegate Bar. In due course, the mother died but she was buried beside her husband under the east window of Holy Trinity church.

It is said that the ghostly figures are those of the nursemaid and the distraught mother, who is still trying to bring her child from its grave in a plague-pit to lie at the side of its father. But she never succeeds and the child is always taken back to the plague-pit beyond the city walls, hence the signs of deep anguish from both its mother and its nursemaid.

The sightings were very numerous during the final years of the last century; indeed, it is said that many congregations were entertained more by these ghosts than by the services they attended. The hauntings seem to have come to an end after alterations to the church and the rebuilding of the present chancel in 1890. Even so, visitors do speak of the cold and death-like atmosphere of this church; it is built on ground which has been hallowed for centuries and reports of further hauntings continue to be made.

26 York
The Legend of Dick Turpin

Dick Turpin is probably Britain's most famous highwayman and much of his renown comes from a story about his legendary ride from London to York on a splendid horse called Black Bess.

Although he was not a Yorkshireman, Turpin has several connections with York and East Yorkshire; he lived for a time in a village overlooking the Humber, and after a trial at York Assizes in 1739, was imprisoned in the condemned cell at York Debtors Prison. Later he was hanged at York Tyburn on the Knavesmire which is now the location of York racecourse.

Dick Turpin was buried in St George's churchyard, York, where his tombstone can still be seen. From time to time, fresh flowers are placed upon his grave and the inscription was recently enhanced to make it more legible. Clearly he is not forgotten, but what is the truth about this romantic figure and his famous 209-mile gallop on Black Bess?

To begin with, Turpin did not make that renowned gallop from London, and furthermore, he was not a romantic hero. He was a coward, a rogue, a poacher, a thief, a burglar, a rapist, a sadist and a killer. That he was evil and dangerous is never in doubt and so it is worth examining his early life to see whether there is any substance in the legendary Turpin.

Richard Turpin was born on 21 September 1705 at Hempstead in Essex. His elder sister and mother were both called Maria; his father, John Turpin, kept an inn

155

known as the Bell, later to be known as the Royal Oak and eventually the Crown.

Young Richard was apprenticed to a butcher at Whitechapel and later established his own business at Waltham Abbey. He married a girl called Hester Palmer at East Ham; she worked as a maid for Turpin's schoolteacher, a man called James Smith, and she was to remain surprisingly faithful to her husband. Like Turpin's father, her father was also an innkeeper, and ran a hostelry at Clay Hill, Enfield.

By all accounts, young Turpin was a skilled butcher and could have made a success of his business, but very early in his career he decided that there was no need to purchase livestock for slaughter. He would simply steal them instead, and he began with an entire herd of beasts. His theft was rapidly discovered and as this was a hanging offence, he fled to a more northerly point of Essex. But his name was circulated as a wanted man and he found himself unable to secure lawful employment. He therefore became a robber to sustain himself and hit upon the brilliant idea of robbing bands of smugglers who operated in the forests of the region. He robbed them by pretending he was a Revenue Officer and seizing their goods 'in the King's name'.

His logic was that his activities would never be reported to the authorities but he had overlooked the fact that the smugglers knew most of the Revenue Officers and they soon realized he was an interloper. If they caught him, their revenge would be savage – indeed, tough retribution had been threatened – and so he fled again, this time returning to the Waltham area where he formed a gang. He and his gang lived in a cave in Epping Forest and stole deer which they sold to venison-dealers in London. But the irregular income from this enterprise was insufficient and so Turpin and his pals joined the notorious Gregory's Gang. This was a gang of former poachers run by a man called Samuel Gregory.

They were brutal men, burglars and robbers, who had armed themselves with pistols and who were never afraid to use violence against any householder who resisted them. They would also break into churches, warehouses, shops and any other premises where valuables could be found and sold to crooked dealers. One Saturday night in February 1735, Turpin and four other rogues smashed their way into the home of an elderly widow at Loughton in Essex and threatened to murder her by holding her over a blazing fire if she did not reveal where her money was hidden. They took over £100 as well as silver-plate and other valuables. The following Tuesday, they broke into the home of a wealthy farmer at Edgwarebury, near Edgware, tied up the maids and men-servants and poured a kettle of boiling water over the farmer's head. Next, they pulled his trousers down and sat him on a fire. Then they raped a maid called Dorothy Street, 'all using her in a most barborous manner', and finally looted the house before leaving the family tightly bound. Mr Lawrence, the farmer in question, was so badly treated that it was doubted whether he would recover.

The attack on Mr Lawrence's farm was the first in a long series of similar brutal attacks on outlying farms and country-houses situated in what is now part of London, but which was then the rural suburbs. Eventually, a reward of £100 was offered for the apprehension of this gang.

Then Westminster peace-officers learned that the gang met in a local ale-house, the Punch House in King Street, and they laid in wait for the men who had become known as the Country Robbers. Turpin, with three colleagues, arrived for a drink and the peace-officers moved in. There followed a tremendous fight in which cutlasses were used, and Turpin's three friends, Fielder, Rose and Wheeler, were caught. Wheeler turned King's evidence, and upon his testimony Fielder and Rose were executed at Tyburn on 10 March 1735. Turpin however had escaped – he had climbed out of a window during the confusion, stolen a horse and galloped to freedom.

That horse, by the way, was not the famous Black Bess, but it was then that Turpin adopted the life of a highwayman, operating with a former member of Gregory's gang called Rowden. They became known as Turpin the Butcher and Rowden the Pewterer and they were a busy pair. On Sunday 16 August that year, they carried out seven robberies either of coaches or gentlemen on horseback on the road between Putney and Kingston Hill. Later, they turned their attention to Surrey but became so well-known that they had to move into Kent to avoid capture.

They were bold too, on one occasion riding through the middle of Blackheath in defiance of the authorities. Their exploits in that area became legendary, and on one occasion Turpin held up a smartly-dressed horseman who laughed at him – it was another highwayman called Tom King and the two men promptly decided to work together. We do not know what became of Rowden the Pewterer at this time, although in July 1737 he was arrested and transported for life.

Throughout his period as a highwayman, Turpin lived in hiding in a cave, said to be between the King's Oak and the Loughton Road in Epping Forest, and it seems that his wife, Hester, remained faithful to him throughout these escapades. She would bring him food when he was in hiding and one account says that his cave was dry and carpeted with straw, hay and dry leaves, and when discovered by the authorities, was found to contain some clean shirts, stockings and female clothing, as well as food and bottles of wine.

By 1737, Turpin had become more dangerous arming himself with a carbine and some slugs as well as his pistols, and there is an account of him killing a man who discovered his retreat in Epping Forest. His rate of robbery rose until he was committing at least one crime per day, and in May 1737 there is some confusion as to whether Turpin shot and killed his friend, Tom King. Certainly a man called King was accidentally shot dead by Turpin in the yard of an inn called the Red Lion at the corner of Whitechapel Road and Leman Street in London.

What did emerge about Turpin's method of operation was that he often robbed unarmed people, even though he was himself heavily armed with pistols and other weapons. Many of his actions were regarded as very cowardly and he showed indications of being a cruel bully – his earlier attack on the elderly widow is just one example.

Even so, some accounts of the time gave him grudging praise because he continued with his business as a highwayman even though he was well-known and even though he was high on the list of wanted criminals. He seemed to have no fear of the law, capture or death by hanging.

By the summer of 1737 his exploits resulted in a proclamation in the *London Gazette* of 25 June which read:

> His Majesty was pleased to promise his most gracious pardon to any of the Accomplices of Richard Turpin who shall discover him, so that he may be apprehended and convicted of the Murder, or any of the robberies he has committed; as likewise, a reward of £200 to any person or persons who shall discover the said criminal so that he may be apprehended and convicted as aforesaid; over and above all other rewards to which they may entitled.

Turpin was described as a small man, only 5' 9'' tall, with high cheek-bones, a pointed chin and a narrow, tapering face heavily pitted with smallpox scars. He was very swarthy with dirty, greasy black hair and was not at all good-looking. Posters bearing his description and announcing the reward were distributed over a wide area with remarkable speed. They were read avidly, for this was a huge sum at that time and it indicates the authorities' determination to arrest Turpin. It had some effect – Turpin realized that even his friends and acquaintances might be tempted to betray him for such money.

He left the London area and some accounts suggest he spent a short time in the Netherlands. Very soon, however, he returned and made for the north of England, thinking he would be safe there. After spending three months in Long Sutton, Lincolnshire he arrived in East Yorkshire, apparently believing this was a quiet area where he would be safe from pursuit. For a while, he stayed at the Ferry House Inn at Brough, and then at North Cave before settling in a village called Welton.

This is a surprisingly pretty village with a pond with weeping-willow and ducks, a small stream which disppears beneath the road, a church dedicated to St Helen overlooking the green and some charming red brick cottages. It lies on the southern tip of the Wolds overlooking the Humber and is some four miles from the northern end of the Humber Bridge, just off the A63 between North Cave and North Ferriby.

Here he was not known as Dick Turpin. He called himself John Palmer and told the local people that he had come from Lincolnshire to settle in Yorkshire. He created for himself the character of a country gentleman skilled in horsemanship and soon earned the reputation of being a superb rider, a high-class dealer in horses and a competent judge at shows. There is every reason to believe that Turpin could have lived quietly in Welton in his disguise as John Palmer, even though some horse-owners in that area did report losing valuable animals.

We do not know whether or not Turpin was ever suspected of being the thief, but his natural roughness and bullying nature was to betray him. After a shooting expedition one day, he returned home much the worse for drink and got into an argument with a neighbour. He lost his temper and deliberately shot one of his neighbour's fighting cocks. When the owner complained, Turpin retorted that if he didn't be quiet, he would shoot him too. He went into the local inn, The Green Dragon, then known as The Green Man, to drink away his temper but was immediately arrested and accused of brawling. The Green Dragon has therefore entered folk history as the place where Dick Turpin was arrested and where he spent his final hours of freedom. Once, you could look at the cellar trap-door he allegedly used to attempt an escape, or the window from which he leapt onto the back of Black Bess, waiting outside. Today, the inn bears a plaque inside to remind us of its role in the Turpin legend.

Following his arrest at The Green Dragon, Turpin was put in gaol pending an appearance at Beverley Quarter

Sessions. His arrest prompted enquiries to be made into his past. He said he was called John Palmer and that he had come from Long Sutton in Lincolnshire, but would admit nothing else. The local people, both in Long Sutton and Welton, admitted they knew nothing of his background and so it was realized that the rough Palmer was something of a mystery man.

Enquiries intensified and there were vague rumours that he had escaped from police custody or even prison at some earlier time. Then a report of a horse-theft alerted the authorities. Turpin then said he had lived with his father and sister in Long Sutton and that he'd left because of debts. Enquiries there, however, revealed no such family of Palmers, except for a John Palmer who had left after being suspected of stealing horses, cattle and sheep and who was wanted for theft of a horse. The outcome was that Turpin was charged with stealing a black mare who was blind in one eye; it was alleged he had taken it from Heckington Common near Sleaford in Lincolnshire. For anyone found guilty, that crime carried the death penalty.

'John Palmer' was committed for trial at York Assizes and two constables, George Smith and John Milner, had the task of escorting him from Beverley to York. While awaiting his trial, he was incarcerated in a cell at York Castle, now the Castle Museum, and in that time decided he should work towards his acquittal. He wrote to his brother-in-law in Hempstead to ask for a reference as to his good character, and signed the letter in the name of John Palmer. But the letter had not been prepaid and so Turpin's brother-in-law, not recognizing the handwriting, refused to pay the surcharge of sixpence due upon it, and declined to accept it. By one of those coincidences that occur in detective stories, the letter was seen by Turpin's old headmster, James Smith, who recognized the writing as that of his former pupil. He must have known of Turpin's reputation and it might be suggested that he was anxious to obtain the £200 reward still being offered, so he took the letter to a magistrate to obtain permission to open it. And so it was realized that the notorious wanted criminal, Dick Turpin, was in custody at York under an assumed name. Smith went along to the trial to undertake the official identification but we do not know whether he received the reward for his efforts.

Turpin appeared at the Assizes under the name of John Palmer and was convicted in that name, even though news of his real identity brought huge crowds to the prison. People came to boast that they had seen Dick Turpin; already he had the makings of a folk hero, and if he was a coward during life, it is recorded that he met his inevitable death, upon being convicted of stealing a horse, in a very brave and almost showman-like manner.

He was in gaol for twenty-six further days during which time he joked and drank with his gaolers and received many visitors, but he refused to confess any earlier crimes to a visiting priest. On the day before his execution, he bought a new frock-coat and some new shoes, then gave the hangman £3. 10s. (£3.50) to be divided between the five men who would follow him as mourners. They were to be given black hatbands and mourning-gloves to be worn during the procession to the gallows. He also left a ring and some other belongings to a woman in Lincolnshire who had befriended him. The reports do not mention his long-suffering wife.

On the morning of his execution, he travelled from the castle to the Knavesmire in an official cart, called a tumbril. He made light of his last trip through York, bowing to the women and flourishing his hat to the large crowd of mourners and admirers who followed, but when he had to mount the scaffold, it is said that his left leg trembled. He stamped it on the ground to halt its movements and so avoid any suggestion that he was frightened. He then launched into a long conversation with his executioner; it lasted half-an-hour, at which the crowd became restless. They wanted some action! He placed the rope around his neck, climbed the ladder to the scaffold (or three-legged horse as it was sometimes called) and before the executioner could carry out his work, threw himself from the heights. He was killed instantly, instead of being slowly strangled to death as happened to some victims.

For a day and a night, Turpin's body lay in the Blue Boar

Inn, Castlegate, York and was then buried in St George's churchyard. But that night it was exhumed by grave-robbers who wanted it for dissection, but because Turpin was already a hero, some of his supporters rescued the corpse and reburied it, this time among quicklime so that it would be useless for medical research.

Some accounts say he shared his grave with another executed villain, while the romance associated with Turpin says he shared it with Black Bess, his faithful horse. The probability is that he was buried alone.

That Dick Turpin was a villain is never in doubt, but in spite of his cruelties and killings, he did become a legend almost immediately. Even as he was being led to his death at York's Knavesmire, that legend was beginning. Very soon, false and idealistic Robin Hood-type stories about his generosity, his kind treatment of his victims and his cavalier behaviour were circulating throughout Britain. They were all false tales, just as the famous ride from London to York never occurred. None the less, some people will point to a place on York racecourse where his gallant horse, Black Bess, expired after her famous gallop from London, and at Stillingfleet between York and Selby, the villagers would show you the stream along which he rode and the gate over which his horse jumped during the last tiring miles of that ride. Some would even point out a nick in the top bar of the gate, said to have been knocked out by one of Bess's hooves.

However, there was a similar ride. It was undertaken by another highwayman, William 'Swift Nick' Nevison who was a romantic character of high breeding, a true Gentleman of the Road. In the spring of 1676, almost thirty years before Turpin was born, Nevison was accused of robbing a man in Gads Hill, Surrey at 4 a.m. one morning. He claimed he was in York at 7.45 p.m. that same day when he actually spoke to the Lord Mayor who was playing bowls in Marygate; the Lord Mayor could recall the incident, so how could he have committed that robbery? Could anyone, asked Nevison, have committed robbery at Gads Hill in Kent at 4 a.m. and yet be in York less than sixteen hours later? After all, even the speedy stagecoaches took four days! The result was that the jury refused to believe the feat was possible and acquitted Nevison. Later, he was to admit that, in fact, he had made the journey, covering some 209 miles in under sixteen hours to create his alibi, albeit changing horses regularly *en route*.

That story of Nevison was used as the basis for a book written by Harrison Ainsworth. It was called *Rookwood* and was published in 1834, but in the story Ainsworth featured Dick Turpin as the hero and wrongly attributed the ride to him, with considerable use of so-called novelist's licence.

He was to attribute some more of Nevison's escapades to Turpin too, possibly because the two men had, in fact, shared the same cell and even the same leg-irons in York's Castle prison. But once the legend had started, no one was able to halt it. Even Charles Dickens has Sam Weller singing about Turpin and Black Bess.

So was Black Bess a real horse? By all accounts, Turpin did have a horse called Bess when he was operating in the London region, but her colour is not given. It was Ainsworth who described her as Black Bess, although it is doubtful whether she was ever ridden all the way from York to London, or if she visited the Green Dragon Inn at Welton where Turpin was arrested. It is probable, however, that Turpin did occasionally make the long trip to London, albeit at a leisurely pace; sometimes he went to see his father who was also a horse-thief.

But York has several genuine relics of Turpin; a visit to the Castle Museum will reveal his cell and some of the irons which held him. A house in Fulford is the former Wheatsheaf Tavern, an inn favoured by Turpin; it is said that he rested here after Black Bess collapsed on the Knavesmire while another of his favourite hostelries is now the British Home Stores in York city centre. Yorkshire, like other parts of Britain, had several 'Turpin Leaps' and there are several other houses and inns at which he and his famous horse are said to have stayed.

And there is, of course, his tombstone, even if it does bear the name of John Palmer. The inscription reads:

John Palmer, otherwise Richard Turpin. The notorious highwayman and horse stealer, executed at

Tyburn, April 7th, 1739 and buried at St George's Churchyard.

His criminal career was very short, only about nine years, and he was not yet 35 when he died. But he is now a world famous character, a fascinating mixture of truth and folk legend.

27   York
The Horn of Ulphus

York Minster contains many treasures. They are far too numerous to list in a book of this kind, but one of them has provided a pleasing folk story.

The treasure in question is the legendary horn of Ulphus, known also as Ulph's horn and it is more than 1,000 years old. The huge ivory horn is more than two feet long, open at one end and tapering to a fine point at the other. It is not a true horn, however; it is thought to be the tusk of either a mammoth or an elephant. It is exquisitely decorated with a broad band of beautifully engraved silver gilt around the rim, and there is a further, narrower band around the body of the horn close to its pointed end, with a silver knob upon the base. The gilt work dates from the seventeenth century.

The silver gilt is not the original decoration. The horn was formerly mounted in gold, but during the time of Cromwell it fell into the hands of the Puritans who were bent on desecrating everything which hinted of religious adornment. It was removed from York Minster and stripped of its fine gold engravings. We are not told what became of that gold nor the whereabouts of the horn during its absence.

What is known, however, is that the horn passed into the custody of Lord Henry Fairfax. He was a nephew of Lord Thomas Fairfax, the English general who commanded the army which defeated Charles I at the Battle of Naseby in 1645. In 1675, Lord Henry restored the horn to its rightful place in York Minster, after arranging for it to be reset with silver-gilt ornamentation. That adornment can still be seen on the horn which is now on show among other treasures in the Undercroft of York Minster.

The man who gave the horn to York Minster was called Ulphus although he is now widely referred to as merely Ulph. He was said to be a relative of the famous King Canute and was the son of a Danish king called Thoraldi. It is known that he was king or chieftain of a portion of north-east England after the Danish invasion; his kingdom was part of Deira, probably a part of what is now West Yorkshire or even part of the North Yorkshire Dales. Even so, there is a good deal of uncertainty about precisely which Ulph donated the famous horn because Ulph or Ulf was a common name among the occupying Danes.

One village which boasts links with Ulph is Ulrome, which lies on the coast between Bridlington and Hornsea. It is part of local folklore that the village is named in his honour.

Ulph was known to have survived into old age, and he had four sons. The eldest was called Adelbert and upon Ulph's death, he was expected to succeed his father as king. But Adelbert was killed in battle before he could claim his inheritance, and so Ulph was presented with a problem about a successor. His three remaining sons all wanted to inherit his kingdom, his vast estates and his wealth and this caused them to fight. They quarrelled bitterly, even during their father's lifetime, and their constant arguments caused great distress to Ulph. Worse still was their unseemly behaviour – Kerdic became a drunkard, Torfrid spent his days hunting and enjoying himself instead of working while the youngest, Edmund, was regarded as a wily coward. In Ulph's opinion, none was suited to the high office of king; none was fit to inherit the throne which had been passed from father to son. No matter how hard he tried, Ulph could not resolve the situation to his satisfaction.

Then, after spending some time in quiet reflection in the Yorkshire dales, he produced a fine idea – he would bequeath his estates to his granddaughter. She was called Adelwynne and was the child of his deceased eldest son. After Adelbert's death, the girl had come to live with Ulph and his wife Queen Helena, and they had come to know the girl very well indeed. In fact, she regarded the old king almost as a father rather than a grandfather. Had Adelbert lived to inherit his kingdom, Adelwynne would have been the eventual benefactor and so Ulph's idea seemed a sound one. She could marry her cousin, Edwy, and then reign over the kingdom.

But this suggestion infuriated the three sons. They were wild with anger and made their views known to the unhappy girl. She was frightened by them and went to discuss the matter with her troubled grandfather. There is an old poem which serves as a reminder of their discussion. Ulph told her:

> Kerdic hath no wit but wine wit;
> Torfrid is a son of Cain;
> Edmund is a wily coward,
> And the dead shall not come again.
> Thou shalt wed thy cousin, Edwy,
> And by Woden, thou shalt reign!

But Adelwynne did not want to reign and although she accepted that her three uncles were unfit to wear the crown, she did suggest an heir to Ulph's kingdom. She told the aged king to give his lands and wealth to Christ so that everyone could have a share in Ulph's kingdom.

> Give to Christ the land of Deira,
> Let the church the people guard;
> So that all shall dwell securely,
> And thy spirit have reward.
> Be not angered, think upon it,
> My grandfather and my Lord.

Ulph was visibly moved by the girl's proposal and said that she was better than any son, but he did act upon her suggestion. He took his largest and finest drinking-horn which was fashioned from the best ivory and decorated with exquisite gold, and rode to York Minster.

At the minster, he filled the horn to its brim with wine and then knelt before the high altar to drink every drop. When the horn was drained, he laid it upon the altar and said that it had to remain with the church for all time as a sign that he, Ulph, had given his lands and wealth to the Church for the benefit of all people.

> Keep my horn, O Holy Father;
> So from age to age be known,
> Power is a trust from heaven –
> Kings have nothing of their own.
> And never shall a son unworthy
> Sit upon my father's throne.

Almost a thousand years later, that horn is still within York Minster to remind us of a pledge made by an unhappy king long, long ago. But Ulph died a contented man and before departing this earthly kingdom, he asked us all 'to think upon the gift of Ulphus.'

28   York
The Miracles of St William

St William of York, although a quiet and religious man, seems to have attracted an unwarranted amount of trouble from the time he was appointed Archbishop of York. Accounts of his life indicate that he did not cause the problems but that they seemed to manifest themselves around him.

His full name was William FitzHerbert and he was a nephew of King Stephen of England who reigned from 1135 to 1154. His father was Count Herbert and his mother, Emma, was the king's sister.

Little is known of William's early life, but as an adult he became a monk of York Minster. For ten years while Thurstan was archbishop, William was the minster's treasurer and he worked diligently and carefully at his tasks. He was popular with his fellow monks and was regarded as a capable administrator although his career was uneventful. When Archbishop Thurstan died in 1140 the question of a successor arose and William was somewhat astonished to find that he had been elected to the post. The appointment was quickly approved by King Stephen.

From that time, things began to go wrong. The first, a major blow to his prestige, occurred when the Pope objected to his election.

This was aggravated because the entire brotherhood of Cistercian monks in England also objected. Pope Innocent II kept William on tenterhooks by making it known that he had other candidates for the office and there is little doubt that William was very unhappy; there were occasions of violent opposition to him with some churches being set on fire, while the Cistercian monks of Yorkshire continued their objections on the grounds that his election had been too strongly influenced by the English king. Finally, the Pope decided that William should be removed from office; none the less, he was consecrated as archbishop but to no effect. His reign as archbishop ended in 1147 when the Cistercian Pope, Eugenius III formally deposed him. His place was taken by Henry Murdac, who was abbot of Fountains Abbey in the Yorkshire Dales.

During his unhappy years in office, however, William had endeared himself to the people. They loved him and could not understand why he was being made to suffer in this way; they had come to regard him as almost saintly. That he was a very good man is not in doubt; he was an adviser and friend to all and a source of spiritual strength to both monks and ordinary people. When Murdac's name was announced as successor, many of William's angry supporters marched to Fountains Abbey and set fire to some of its buildings, an act deplored by William.

Perhaps glad to be rid of the burden of office, William retired to resume his former role of monk and man of prayer. He kept in touch with the simple people and became a highly respected and much-loved figure in and around York. Then, in 1153, Archbishop Murdac died.

Once again, the question of a successor arose, and once again the monks of York Minster put forward the name of their beloved William. By now, there was a new Pope, Anastasius IV and he called William to Rome to discuss the appointment. It seems that William told the Pope about his previous troubles and his unjust treatment, and on this occasion, even though William was now an elderly man, the Pope reappointed him as Archbishop of York.

News reached the delighted people of York well ahead of William and so by the time he reached the city on his triumphant return to the minster, a huge crowd was waiting to greet him and watch him ride into York through the city gates. The crowd stretched down to Ouse Bridge, which was then a flimsy wooden structure. Everyone was cheering and waving, and as William's procession came into view, the crowd pressed forward to catch a glimpse of him. But that rickety old bridge had not been built to withstand such crowds and there was a terrible splintering of wood as the entire structure collapsed. Men, women, children, horses and dogs were all thrown into the deep waters below. The shouts of happiness turned into cries of fear and alarm as the swirling waters threatened to drown hundreds of people.

William witnessed the event and, so the story goes, he did not panic. Instead he simply halted, bowed his head in prayer and made the sign of the cross. Instantly, the turbulent waters changed into a solid support.

Somehow, they did not draw those people into their depths but thickened to form a virtual bridge and at the same time rose to the height of the adjoining banks. The astonished people managed to clamber to safety and the accounts say that the only casualty was one horse which suffered a broken leg. Not a single man, woman or child was lost.

This was immediately acclaimed as a miracle and a chapel was later built beside the river at this point. The stature of William soared in York and its district, but his sufferings, his age and his long journey to Rome and back had taken its toll. Added to this was the fact that the heavy duties of archbishop were far from easy. Within less than a month, William fell ill and died. The year was now 1154 and he was buried in the nave of the minster.

But not even his death was free from trouble. Rumours began to circulate that William had been poisoned by his rivals and this served only to enhance his reputation. His gentle and holy character and his total devotion to God did have its rewards, however, because in 1227, seventy-three years after his death, William FitzHerbert was canonized by Pope Gregory IX and became St William of York. His feast day is 8 June.

In the years that followed, pilgrims began to visit his tomb in the minster and this prompted the authorities to reinter him in a more elevated position. It took some years to effect this and so, before a congregation which included King Edward I, Queen Eleanor and noblemen from the whole of England as well as church dignitaries, the bones of St William were removed from their resting-place in the nave and reburied behind the high altar. The date was 8 January 1283. A shrine was established in his honour and this continued to attract pilgrims until it was abolished during the Reformation. Later, however, it seems that the saint's bones were returned to their former resting-place. In May 1732, a York historian called Drake found a leaden casket in the nave containing some bones. It was thought they were those of St William and they were reinterred once more. Today, a splendid and huge stained glass window in the North Choir Aisle, known as the Saint William Window, depicts scenes from the life of York's own saint, including the tale of the broken bridge.

But the miracle of the broken bridge was not his only supernatural achievement. Miracles began to happen to people who visited his tomb and although many were reported, few details have survived. One incident, however, is on record.

Two women were charged with murdering a third and, at that time, one method of determining innocence or guilt was trial by ordeal. In prison awaiting their trial, one of the suspects died, but the other pleaded total innocence.

The judges decided she must suffer trial by ordeal, and that the trial must take place within York Minster. Attendants heated an iron bar until it glowed red and the suspect was ordered to pick it up in one hand and carry it three paces. She had then to run to an altar where a priest would quickly bandage her hand. She did this; the priest sealed the bindings with the church's own wax so that no one could loosen it. Three days later, she was to report to judges, again assembled in the minster, when the bindings on her hand would be undone. In accordance with the rules of trial by ordeal, if there was no sign of burning and no blisters, then she would be declared innocent. If, however, there was a blister or other injuries resulting from holding the red-hot iron bar, then she would be deemed guilty.

Unfortunately, the bindings revealed a large blister on the palm of her hand and so the judges pronounced her guilty and sentenced her to death. When asked if she had any last wish before sentence was carried out, she requested permission to pray at the tomb of St William.

This was granted – but when she arose after her prayers, the blister had vanished. There were no traces of burns or injuries when she showed her hand to the judges.

They did not know what action to take, for they had already pronounced her guilty, and so the case was referred to the High Court where its bench of learned judges decided that she must be innocent.

'If God and His Holy Saints judge her innocent,' the chairman decided, 'We will not condemn her.'

And so the legend of St William began. Thousands made pilgrimages to his shrine within York Minster, many miracles were reported, and today his name continues to feature in the history of York.